Diggers & Dreamers

Edited by

Sarah Bunker   **Chris Coates**

Andy Hill   **David Hodgson**

Jonathan How   **Christine Watson**

DIGGERS AND DREAMERS PUBLICATIONS

©
**Diggers & Dreamers
Publications
2001**

First published
2001
D&D Publications
BCM Edge
London
WC1N 3XX

ISBN
0 9514945 6 2
Paperback

Distribution
Edge of Time Ltd
BCM Edge
London
WC1N 3XX
(07000) 78053

Printing (contents)
Greenwood Recycled
Printing
(01484) 844841

Printing (cover)
Buckingham Colour
Press
(01280) 824000

Typesetting and Layout
Jonathan How
(0870) 4442566
Sarah Bunker
(01363) 877228

Acknowledgements: Thank you to all the communities, housing co-ops and other organisations that have responded to our requests for information. Once again we've been to several places for our meetings in the last two years, so grateful thanks to everyone at Old Hall, Some People in Leicester, Little Grove, Beech Hill and Redfield for being such generous hosts.

INTRODUCTION

Global warming, environmental disaster, Agenda 21, Kyoto.......... at the dawn of the 21st Century Sustainable development has become the buzzword on everyones' lips. In intentional communities we have been trying for 25 years or more to find ways to live socially & environmentaly sustainable lifestyles. This year's new format directory has a bank of sustainability icons as eco-indicators of a group's environmental impact. And whilst of the communities listed only small numbers have invested in eco-technologies (solar power 20%, electricity generation 13%) the majority have social ecologies with very high elements of sustainablity built in (shared utilities 83%, shared meals 76%, organised recycling schemes 75%, food growing 60%, shared vehicles 44%). In the challenge to find ways to live in harmony with our planet, communal living has a crucial role to play - sharing resources may prove to be a more socially sustainable model for future communities than any number of eco-gadgets.

For those of you who have bought previous issues of D&D and are wondering where all the articles have gone, some have migrated to our website and some of them will now appear in new Diggers & Dreamers Publications, the first of which — Utopia Britannica — is now in bookshops. We hope you enjoy the new edition.

Live Simply, Live Lightly, Live Communally!

Frequently Asked Questions

About Communal Living

The following pages contain some of the frequently asked questions posed at living in community weekends and by potential applicants who visit communities in their quest to find an appropriate community. The answers are by no means complete but will, we hope, provide you with a stepping stone for further investigation.

Joining an Existing Community ⟶

What financial input is expected of me?

Some communities require that you buy your space from an outgoing member. This can either be on a cash lump sum basis or by raising a mortgage in the traditional way. The outgoing member takes this money with them. Having joined, you then pay a maintenance sum on a monthly basis to cover heat, light, power etc. Other communities require no capital sum but rent instead. This is usually higher than maintenance because it often covers a mortgage repayment as well as heat, light etc. A third type of community may be a charity and you live there in return for work done. In these last two cases you take no money with you when you leave. For income-sharing communities you might be expected to bring your capital into the community as collateral. In communities where meals are eaten collectively you might log your meals and pay for them at the end of the month. All communities work a variation on the above sytems.

What kind of work commitment is expected?

This varies, but might typically be between ten and fifteen hours per week. There may be a voluntary element. Some communities differentiate between domestic chores and other work. Three hours domestic, ten other etc. In all cases, consideration is given to fairness.

What kind of skills am I expected to bring in to a community situation?

There is a pool of skills in every community which is constantly changing as members leave and arrive. Practical skills are always in demand from painters to pipe benders, bread makers to bed makers, roofers to rolfers. What skills do you have? A willingness to share your skills is always a bonus, so too is a willingness to learn.

Will I be able to change from one living space to another within the community once I have moved in?

There may be systems set up to allow this to happen. Find out what they are. You may have to wait for someone else to move out first. One very large income sharing community in Denmark (150 people) has a moving around group, comprising a bunch of members who vet all applications from members who want a change of space. Very well organised. Smaller communities will have similar, less rigid methods. In rent-based communities it is not uncommon for one person to move and set off a chain reaction whereby all move around.

How does the community approach conflict resolution?

Ideally, every community will have a system in place for resolving conflict. There are basically three levels of approach. One-to-one face-to-face open discussion between aggrieved parties. Face-to-face meeting with a third party facilitator or mediator chosen by agreement between the conflicting parties, or a mediation group selected by the community and agreed by the aggrieved parties. Individuals may take their problem to the group, who then decide on the best method of approach and who co-ordinate and facilitate the process of resolution.

How are decisions made?

Secular communities tend to be non-hierarchical. Consensus is the norm with vote or veto used as a last resort.

Can I expect support from the community?

There will always be support in one shape or form from individuals living within any community. The extent of this support will depend very much on the nature, or level, of support required by the party needing that support. From personal experience, if an individual in need of support leans too heavily on other community members the tendency is for those members to back off after a while. If you need a counsellor or therapist, go to one. Some communities have co-counselling groups set up. If you need support because of a physical difficulty or change of circumstances you will need to negotiate with the group you join.

What is the community's philosophy toward children and education?

The long-standing communities have tried most methods of education over their lifetimes. Current philosophy is nearly always open to discussion and change. Make sure you discuss your ideas to the full. Find out how enthusiastic, welcoming and supportive other members are to your ideas for change - or not.

How long does it take to join?

Longer than you think. You cannot rush your application. Wheels turn slowly in communities, sometimes very slowly. The more you try and rush your process the less likely are your chances of being accepted. If you are desperate for housing then sort it out, at least temporarily, before applying.

What arrangements does the community have for personal visitors?

This varies from community to community. In order to prevent personal visitors from overstaying their welcome, time limitations are often placed on them.

These limitations vary depending on whether or not the visitor is occupying a community guest room or living within the personal space of the sponsoring friend. The former limitations are shorter on the grounds that the guest room will be needed by others in due course. You or your visitor may have to pay their share of food, heat, light and costs.

Can I bring my pets with me?

This is more contentious than you might expect. Negotiate with your chosen community as there may be arrangements in place regarding pets.

How do people in communities earn a living?

There is a difficulty in working full time whilst still retaining commitment to the community. Some people overcome this by working from home or by working part-time, or running community businesses. Whatever your preferences are, you must check out the issues of transport and the closeness to potential work, especially if the community is a rural one.

Setting Up a Community with Others

What kind of ideologies and social structures do embryonic communities discuss?

Check out the descriptions of embryonic and existing communities on in this book and on the Diggers and Dreamers website to find out the whole range of ideological focuses encompassed. In general, these are the issues you will be discussing.

How long can I expect to be in discussion with an embryonic group?

Anything up to two years. Longer than this and you have to ask yourself: is this going anywhere? There are plenty of people who prefer dreaming to digging!

How do we go about finding an appropriate property?

All UK councils have a buildings at risk register. This is a list of properties in need of repair from country homes to architectural follies to farm houses, old castles and the like. A rich source of properties, some of which are for sale. The list provides addresses and contact names and numbers as well as details of the state of repair.

Contact the local planning department for more details.

Other routes are low-impact living or ecological buildings, perhaps self-build.

Where would I go to find other people who want to start a community?

It's hard work starting a community by yourself! Ideas become better developed when they've been fashioned by several people. Visit some communities first (see http://www.diggersanddreamers.org.uk) - you may meet some like-minded people. Once you've got a handful of people and a clearer concept of what you want to set up, then place an advert on the 'Places needing People' page of the website. Advertise in the national and local papers. Book onto one of the living in community weekends or week-long workshops run by some of the existing communities. Check out the above website for details.

Are there any financial organisations sympathetic to co-operative/community living?

Yes, they include Radical Routes, Rootstock (see Network/Support section, p 218), the Triodos bank and the Ecology Building Society (see Useful Contacts, p 224).

How long does it take to leave if I decide to move away?

Probably at least a month's notice if you are in a rented situation. For those of you who may have invested capital then the process will be longer. If the community chooses the new member for your space, not you, then this can take time. See above.

THUMBNAIL BOOK REVIEWS:
FULL REVIEWS AVAILABLE ON OUR WEBSITE
www.diggersanddreamers.org.uk

Utopia Britannica : British Utopian Experiments 1325 — 1945
Chris Coates. Diggers & Dreamers Publications, 2001. Available from Edge of Time

If you thought that ours was the first generation to try to change the world then think again. This archaeology of dreams explores every corner of these islands detailing over 500 utopian experiments in a comprehensive historical gazetteer and tells the stories of our utopian ancestors from early Christian Sects to the foundation of the welfare state. Less a catalogue of broken dreams, more a rough guide to a utopian future.

Eurotopia. Directory of Intentional Communities and Ecovillages in Europe
Eurotopia, 2000. (English language edition) Available from Edge of Time.
Communal living and Ecovillage projects from Iceland to Israel and all ports of call in between, in all some 336 communities in 23 countries are detailed from those with only a handful of members just starting out to large well-established groups with years of communal experience. With a great intro section on how to visit and what to expect when you get there, this is the definitive guide to utopian Europe.

The Sustainable Community; A Practical Guide

Hockerton Housing Project, 2001.
Available from Edge of Time.
In a densely packed, magazine format, the Hockerton Housing Project have distilled their experiences of putting into practice the principles of ecological living. From *What is a sustainable community?* through to *Selecting green furnishing and household goods*, the guide takes you step-by-step from the depths of your armchair to the door of your own eco-community.

Utopian England. Community Experiments 1900-1945

Dennis Hardy. E. & F.N. Spon, 2000.
England in the early 20th century was rich in utopian ventures, diverse and intriguing in their scope and aims. Two world wars, an economic depression, and the emergence of fascist states in Europe were all a spur to idealists to create sanctuaries for new and better lives.
Utopian England explores this fascinating history of utopian ideals, the lives of those pursued them, and the communities they created.

Pueblos Vivos: the guide to communal living in Spain (in Spanish)

106 pp, Vida Comunitaria, 2001
Articles, descriptions, resources and bibliography.
http://www.nodo50.org/vidacomunitaria
Order from Loris, Vida Comunitaria, Apdo Correo 1039, Algeciras, 11200 C diz, Spain

**A Guide to Intentional Communities
and Co-operative Living 2000 Edition**
ISBN 0 9602714 8 1, 456pp $30
Fellowhip for Intentional Community.
Lists over 700 communities around the
world but primarily in North America;
33 illustrated articles about community
living plus a recommended reading list of
over 300 titles. Jam-packed resources
section, maps, indexes and more!
http://www.ic.org
also from Community Bookshelf
http://bookshelf.ic.org/

**Designing Utopia. John Ruskin's
Urban Vision for Britain and America**
Michael H. Lang. Black Rose Books. 1999.
www.web.net/blackrosebooks.
The life of John Ruskin; the development of his views on architecture
and urban design, as well as his views on social justice; how his vision
was developed from his writings; and his efforts at practical application of that vision. It also looks at the long line of communities that
have developed from his ideas; from Arts & Crafts colonies to
Co-Housing.

**The Patchwork History of a Community
Growing Up**
General Editor: Brenda Gamlin 120pp, Old
Hall Community, 2000. £5 plus P+P from Old
Hall, c/o Brenda Gamlin (address: p 133)
A patchwork story which celebrates the growth
of Old Hall Community over a quarter of a
century. Neither a chronological history nor a
an in-depth analysis of communal living, nor
merely scenes from the ongoing soap opera
that is life at Old Hall. Rather it is a collection
of memories, accounts and views of individual
members and friends, spanning 26 years.

DIRECTORY OF COMMUNITIES AND NETWORKS

ABOUT THIS DIRECTORY

•••••••••••••••••••••••••••••••••

In the Directory we list existing and embryonic UK communities and Networks which have chosen to have entries. As you will see when you start to read their entries, there is a wide variety of types of communal living groups; some of these groups may work together, some may income share, some may have a spiritual focus, some may not necessarily live under the same roof; whole groups, or people within the groups, may be committed to ideals such as permaculture, veganism, home education and struggling against sexism, racism and homophobia; others may well not.

Remember that there are many other communal groups who are not listed, including countless shared houses, but all the groups in this directory share a desire to be public about their lifestyle; many are looking for new members, and most of them welcome visitors. If you are thinking about living communally and want to experience what these places are like, this is the place to start. If you do decide that you want to visit one or more places then please don't just turn up. Remember that you will be going into people's homes, and it is important to write to them (perhaps letting them know why you are interested) and wait for an invitation to come. Some groups set aside particular dates for welcoming first-time visitors, others welcome volunteers, WWOOFers (Willing Workers On Organic Farms - address on p 224) or run workshops or courses which may be a good way of visiting for the first time, although you probably won't get a flavour of day-to-day communal life. Don't be shy of visiting, though; most groups rely on a stream of visitors to find the new members that are essential for the ongoing life of the community, and a wealth of experiences awaits you!

HOW TO USE THE INDEX, MAP AND DIRECTORY

The Index at the back of the book is intended to help you select the groups you may wish to visit. We have tried, as far as possible, to go by groups' own answers to the questions. A ● is only shown if their answer was definitely "yes". If their answer was "no" or ambiguous then nothing is shown. In such cases it might mean, for example, that they do income share in some way or that they do eat communally occasionally. Where a group's diet is shown as vegetarian (vtn) it means that they never consume any meat (although there's often some ambiguity around fish); and where it is vegan (vgn), that they never consume any animal products.

A letter denotes those communities with a spiritual focus:

A	**Anthroposophy (philosophy of Rudolf Steiner)**
B	**Buddhist**
C	**Christian**
Q	**Quaker**
S	**Spiritual but non-specific**

The numbers on both the index and the map refer to the page number of each group's entry (a few communities did not wish to be shown on the map). Entries are ordered alphabetically.

In the index the column heading 'open in

principle' means that the community in question is open to new members in principle, although there might not be space for new members at present. Names are somewhat abridged in the index.

Some groups did not wish their telephone numbers to be published. Some groups did not want their addresses printed; if you write to them 'care of Diggers & Dreamers' we will forward mail directly (unopened) to them. (Our address is at the front of this book.)

New to this edition are our icons, shown at the bottom of each entry and explained on the next two pages.

DISCLAIMER

The editorial team has always decided that it should trust the groups and allow them to decide, themselves, whether or not they should be included in this directory of communal living. We must point out that we cannot take responsibility for the accuracy of entries, as we are not in a position to verify information sent to us, nor can we be held responsible for anything that may occur to individuals visiting groups as result of reading this directory. Good luck!

DIRECTORY ICONS

We hope that the following icons used in the entries will give you more information — especially about aspects of sustainability. The icons in the embryonic section are in grey since they are aspirations rather than reality.

MONEY

 income sharing community-
all income is shared

 capital required-
capital required from all members

ENERGY USE

 on site electricity generation-
wind, water or solar energy provides some power

 solar power used-
solar used for space and/or water heating

 insulation to a high standard-
buildings are double-glazed and insulated

TRANSPORT

 regular use of bikes for transport

 shared use of vehicles-
carpool or recognised arrangements for sharing private cars

 easy access to public transport-
bus stop and/or train station within easy walking distance

shared utilities-
domestic facilities (eg washing machines) shared

shared workshop-
communal workshop and communally owned tools

organised recycling system

eco-friendly sewage system-
compost toilets, reed beds or other alternatives in use

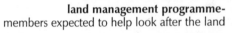

LAND, FOOD, SMOKING and ACCESS

land management programme-
members expected to help look after the land

grow a lot of vegetables-
substantial garden (but not necessarily self-sufficient)

animals reared for food-
livestock reared for human consumption

regular communal meals

policy which restricts smoking-
smoking restricted to certain areas or banned

wheelchair access

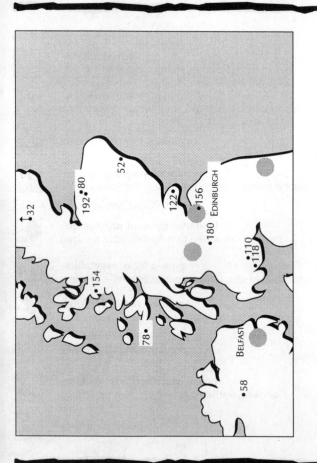

32

192 80

52

122

156

180 EDINBURGH

110
118

154

78

BELFAST

58

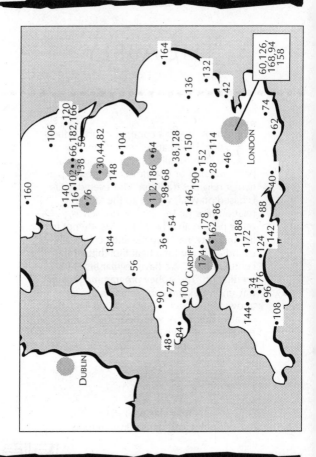

THE ABBEY

The Abbey is a community and educational /retreat centre, offering possibilities for all who follow a spiritual path, whether or not they come from a particular religious tradition. Our everyday life is based on what we see as the four true relationships to: the Divine, our selves, other people and the earth. We attempt to live in a way that is simple and ecologically sound and care for a beautiful thirteenth century house. We have regular times for meditation. The Abbey programme provides day and weekend courses related to the above four aspects of relationship, including creative arts, work with body, mind and emotions, interfaith exploration and alternative economics.

Year started 1981
Ideological focus christian roots

The Green, Sutton Courtenay,
Abingdon, Oxfordshire OX14 4AF England
Electronic Mail admin@theabbeysc.demon.co.uk
World Wide Web http://www.theabbey.uk.com

The rooms are available for hire; the guest
house accommodates fourteen. There are
four acres of grounds, including an organic
vegetable garden.

ASHRAM COMMUNITY

Ashram Community began in 1967, with the intention of developing committed urban communities, which would develop appropriate new forms of Christian community related to urban needs. This led to having inner city Community Houses in the 1970s to 1990s, in Rochdale, Middlesborough, London, Sheffield and Birmingham. There are at present still two inner city community houses in Sheffield. Meanwhile, Ashram developed its community presence in terms of shops and residences. The first of these, the Ashram Centre and New Roots Shop (wholefoods, fruit & veg, Traidcraft) was opened in 1987. The second, the Burngreave Ashram and New Roots Shop was opened in 2001. It is a complex of a shop, two residences, public meeting rooms, offices and basement, plus being the

Year started 1967
Ideological focus radical christian

Diggers & Dreamers 2002/03

Ashram Community
178 Abbeyfield Road,
Sheffield, South Yorkshire S4 7AY England
Telephone 0114 243 6688 **Fax** 0114 243 6688
World Wide Web http://www.ashram.org.uk

base for the Spital Hill Community Learning
Centre. It is hoped that this model of volun-
teer-served shop plus local community base
plus residence for two or three members,
will develop elsewhere. At present, proposals are being completed for a shop/house in
the Parkfield inner city area of Stockton-on
Tees. The common life of Ashram
Community is inspired by the radical styles
of Jesus and the earliest Christians. The
Community sustains this through regional
Branches, half-yearly Weekends and half-
yearly Community General Meetings, plus
Retreats, Holidays, Walks and other occa-
sions. In 2001, the Community wrote and
published a "Discovery Course in Radical
Christianity" called "Journey", which is available to groups in any part of the country.

BALNAKEIL CRAFT VILLAGE

Balnakeil Craft Village was originally a Royal Air Force Early Warning Station, built during the 1950s but made obsolete before it came fully into use. After ten years lying derelict, it was taken over by the local County Council and the buildings initially let to craftspeople but later sold to them on an individual basis. The buildings are typical Ministry of Defence style architecture: single story, concrete block built with flat roofs, and vary in size, but are mostly roomy enough for a shop, workshop and plenty of living accommodation in each. There are about six craft shops/galleries on the site, individually owned, run and mostly open from May to October. There is also a café. Buildings come up for

Year started 1964
Ideological focus crafts

sale from time to time. Living is not communal, nor is there any income sharing, but
the compactness of the site and the remote-
ness of the village lead to a certain feeling of
community, although this has become ——
sadly — more fragmented in recent times .

BEECH HILL COMMUNITY

W e live in a large country house in the rolling Devon hills. Accommodation is both rented and leasehold, in converted outbuildings and in the main house. On our seven acres of land we grow organic fruit and vegetables. We have a paddock with three sheep and chickens, an orchard, a vineyard, a walled garden, a swimming pool, compost toilets and a reed-bed sewage system. Together we run a course centre and spend the income on community projects. We share responsibility for our home and the land on which we live. There is the choice of a shared meal each evening and at least 20 birthdays a year (cake, candles and song). We participate in the wider community, promoting awareness of everyone's impact on the environment, through the local recycling scheme, community open

Year started 1983
Ideological focus ecological

Beech Hill House, Morchard Bishop,
Crediton, Devon EX17 6RF England
Telephone 01363 877228 **Fax** 01363 877587
Electronic Mail beechhill@ukonline.co.uk
World Wide Web http://www.beech-hill.org.uk

days and the parish GMO Concern Group.
Individuals earn their income in the wider
world in journalism, education, building,
complementary health, editing, alternative
ceremonies and nursing; some work from
home. We do not want our community to
be a place of dogmatism, judgement or
preaching. We value our diversity and flexi-
bility. We aim to care for one another and
enjoy life as it happens. We welcome each
others' differences and enjoy visitors and
volunteers - please send an SAE.

BIRCHWOOD HALL COMMUNITY

Birchwood Hall is a large 19th century red brick house near the Malvern Hills. Within our eight acres we have woodlands, a large vegetable garden, orchard and lawns. A converted Coach House is home to an additional six co-op members. There is also a small residential centre called "Anybody's Barn", a registered charity.

The community currently comprises eleven adults and four young children. Most community members have some form of paid employment. Current occupations include: Architect, Photographer, Teacher, Sports administrator, GP, Clinical Psychologist, Civil Servant and Nurse.

A focal point of community life is our daily shared evening meal. We also have weekly meetings where we discuss practical and business issues, exchange ideas or perhaps play a game.

Year started 1971
Ideological focus none

Everyone pays a weekly rent, adjusted to
reflect income and circumstances. Rents
include contributions to a fund we call
"Other than Ourselves", which we allocate
annually to charities and causes.
We live communally because this meets
many of our personal and political needs
and beliefs. We do not try to be self-sufficient and our life is not particularly centred
around rural pursuits. We have a broad
sympathy for many green ideas and causes
and we try to lead an ecologically responsible lifestyle.

BLACKCURRENT
HOUSING CO-OP

We are based in a large town house, which was originally built as a school. We are striving towards a more sustainable lifestyle within the constraints of our urban situation. We share an ethos of nonviolence and respect for each other and the wider community. Some practical applications of this are: all communal food is vegan and organic, and the house is a meat/fish/poultry/egg free zone. We don't keep pets or livestock. We heat the house with woodstoves run on salvaged wood. We have a garden where we grow some of our own food, veganically. Toxic chemicals are not allowed in the house or garden. We homeschool and share childcare and housework. We have no communal TV or radio, preferring to make our own music, play table tennis and create cooperative games. We plan to install solar

Year started 1988
Ideological focus nonviolence

water heating, grow a forest garden and make composting toilets.

The house provides the base for a forming community (see the Anarres entry). However, there are also people living here, who don't intend to join Anarres but are exploring community living or just need somewhere to live. We welcome visitors who would like to work with us and charge £2.50 a day.

BOGNOR REGIS
L'ARCHE COMMUNITY

L'Arche is an international community which builds, or at least aims to build, community among people with and without learning disabilities. Being international it is in fact interfaith but largely it is based on the Christian ethics of the Gospel. Its members range from those for whom L'Arche is their lifetime home, some marrying and having families and living outside the original community houses with people with learning disabilities, to those who stay for 5-10 years and others who come to live and work in the community for a year. Some of its members are former assistants/carers who having left employment have chosen to stay in contact with the community in a particular way continuing to develop relationships and contributing to and receiving from the community. Community events are usually full of life

Year started 1978
Ideological focus christian

Bradbury House
51A Aldwick Road,
Bognor Regis, West Sussex PO21 2NJ England
Telephone 01243 863426 **Fax** 01243 840383
Electronic Mail bognor@larche.org.uk

and energy which leave you exhilarated or
thoroughly exhausted! It is a challenge to
live alongside 9 or 10 other people caring
and supporting each other in many diverse
and often simply basic ways. As an assistant
there is a job to do and skills to learn and as
a friend there is a vast wealth of experiences
to enable personal and spiritual growth. It is
an opportunity to become fully alive and to
share in the highs and lows of human
nature.

BRADWELL OTHONA COMMUNITY

H ere is a place where you can experience a different kind of holiday and go home with a fresh sense of well-being and community. It is inexpensive and our centre is in a beautiful and remote corner of Essex on the River Blackwater. Nearby is the Saxon chapel of St Peter on the Wall which we use for twice daily informal worship. Our year round activities include Art, Music and Drama weeks for all ages, weekends on our environment as well as religious themes and special times of celebration at Easter and Christmas. Our lifestyle is simple and non- dogmatic Christian. We welcome people of all faiths and of none. Our aim is that through open relationships and shared activities away from the pressures of modern life, we will

Year started 1944
Ideological focus christian

East Hall Farm, East End Road, Bradwell-on-Sea
Southminster, Essex CM0 7PN England
Telephone 01621 776564
Electronic Mail centre@othona-bos.org.uk
World Wide Web http://www.othona.org

reach a deeper understanding and accept-
ance of ourselves and others. We welcome
individuals, families, school and church
groups. To find out more, please write, ring
or e-mail.

BRAMBLES
HOUSING CO-OP

Brambles is a home for an eclectic mix of people and animals and a stop over and hanging out point for many more. We have two neighbouring houses, veg patches, fruit trees and wildlife garden. One kitchen is vegan / gluten free, one vegetarian with regular bread and cheese frenzies. We live in a multi-cultural, economically poor but vibrant inner-city area of Sheffield. The Co-op has been running for 10 years, housing over 40 people during that time, with members staying from a few months to several years.

Our current members come from very different cultural and social backgrounds and vary in age from 21-33 but have all come to reject the wage-slavery / day to day drudgery of modern life and instead explore and promote co-operative ways of living. Brambles provides members with a secure,

Year started 1991
Ideological focus ecological

supportive environment from which we
each do our own stuff. The Co-op acts as a
focal point for resources (tat), information
and for various local projects / campaigns,
as well as providing a free meeting space for
local groups. We are planning to open a
resource centre several times a week for use
by the local community along with a radical
library.

Brambles is anarchic and open-minded with
no rotas and few rules but communal meals
generally happen (often for around 10 people) and the recycling eventually gets done.

BRAZIERS ADULT COLLEGE

Founded in 1950, Braziers is a non-religious community and a college. The main house is Strawberry Hill, Gothic in style, and set in 50 acres of unspoilt Oxfordshire countryside. Around a dozen long-term residents with a variety of backgrounds and interests live here and, in addition, there are usually five or six foreign students who come to improve their English and help run the College. Braziers is broadly evolutionist in outlook and has a particular interest in group process and group communication. We run our own educational programme - mainly at weekends - but we are also available as a venue for outside groups. Visitors may either stay in the house or opt to camp in the meadows. There are 22 bedspaces in the house, but camping allows us to accommodate much larger groups. The cooking has a vegetarian emphasis, but

Year started 1950
Ideological focus evolutionist ecological

Braziers Park, Ipsden,
Wallingford, Oxfordshire OX9 6AN England
Telephone 01491 680221 **Fax** 01491 680221
Electronic Mail admin@braziers.org.uk
World Wide Web http://www.braziers.org.uk

meat dishes are also served. Many of the vegetables come from our own organic kitchen garden. One of our newest ventures involves Permaculture. We are working closely with the Permaculture Academy with the intention of running permaculture courses at Braziers and increasing the sustainable output of the land. Low cost work weekends will soon be available for anyone who wants to come and help us with this experiment. The atmosphere at Braziers is informal, relaxed and supportive. Many people come here simply for a break or to complete a personal work project in tranquility.

BRITHDIR MAWR

We are a farm of 165 acres aiming at sustainability. There is a traditional farmhouse with converted outbuildings, plus several functional green design buildings and five eco-homes. We milk goats and keep ducks and chickens. Gardens are large and organic. We use horse power for cart, harrowing and snedding. Fuel is wood. Energy is all from renewable sources. Visit the hostel for up to a week for £5 per night (£2.50 children). We are open to self-catering willing workers. We celebrate the seasons and sing and play music.

Year started 1994
Ideological focus sustainable

Brithdir Mawr,
Newport, Pembrokeshire SA42 0QJ Wales
Telephone 01239 820164
Electronic Mail brithdir@brithdirmawr.freeserve.co.uk
World Wide Web http://www.brithdirmawr.freeserve.co.uk

BROTHERHOOD CHURCH

The Brotherhood Church is a Christian Pacifist Group and has been in existence for over 100 years. Around 1892 it was jointly at Purley in Essex with Tolstoyans.

In 1898 the Tolstoyans in the group decided to move to Whiteway near Stroud in Gloucestershire. The rest of the group, Christian Pacifists, moved to Yorkshire, moving around a bit, but mainly in Yorkshire, the Leeds area. This group was very strong in its opposition to the government during WWI.

Quite a number of the men spent two and a half years in prison for not fighting, others, both men and women went to prison for writing and distributing anti-war leaflets.

This tradition continues to the present day.

Year started 1921
Ideological focus christian/pacifist/ecological

Brotherhood Church
Stapleton,
nr Pontefract, Yorkshire WF8 3DF England
Telephone 01977 620381

Around 1920 members felt the need to
have contact with Mother Earth, a seven
and a half-acre field was bought and bungalows built without any resort to planning
permission.

This land is probably some of the oldest
organic holdings in Britain. Our Members
and Trustees do not all live here at Stapleton
but give their support from all corners of
Britain.

We live out an ecological lifestyle, some
refer to us as Anarchist, but it is really a
Christian Pacifist lifestyle.

We have a large Strawberry Tea Gathering in
early July and usually a smaller evening
event in October. Visitors are welcome at all
times.

CAMPHILL RUDOLF STEINER SCHOOLS

The Camphill-Rudolf Steiner-Schools, which are situated on three estates in Royal Deeside, provide curative education for children with special needs ranging in age from 5 to 19. A total of 150 co-workers live together with 118 pupils in 20 family units: the co-workers share the work that has to be done - teaching, caring, household tasks, gardening, etc. In the traditional Camphill household the child is part of a 'family' unit, which approximates closely to what one might term a 'normal' family environment where there is continuity and consistency of treatment, organisational stability and a sense of personal security. From the foundation of the first Camphill community by Dr Karl König, it has been recognised that all children have strengths

Year started 1940
Ideological focus anthroposophy

Central Office, Murtle House, Bieldside
Aberdeen AB15 9EP Scotland·
Telephone 01224 867935 **Fax** 01224 868420
Electronic Mail b.porter@crss.org.uk
World Wide Web http://www.camphillschools.org.uk

and weaknesses and that it is the responsibility of those working in Camphill settings
to develop the assets that each child pos-
sesses. To that end, an holistic approach is
taken to the individual's physical, psycholog-
ical, social and spiritual needs. At a time
when there is general disquiet at the spiritual bleakness of living in a society preoccu-
pied with short-term and materialistic
concerns, Camphill communities make no
apology for their celebration of Christian
Festivals, their dedication to Christian values
and translating those values into action.

CANON FROME
COURT

The main house and the stable block contain 18 leasehold self-contained living spaces of varying sizes, housing some 30 adults (27-67) and 19 children (0-17). We also have a meeting room for our weekly meetings (decisions by consensus); communal guest rooms; a dairy kitchen for making cheese, yogurt and butter; a 'pot luck' room for a communal meal on Saturdays, high days and holidays, and where we also hold occasional workshops (basketmaking, yoga); the "gym", which is a huge hall, for ceilidhs parties and singing and dance workshops; and a 'shop' for wholefoods and chocolate. There are workshops for metal, wood and basketmaking, not to mention Den's furniture emporium. Our mixed farm supports a variety of animals - dairy and beef cattle, goats, sheep,

Year started 1978
Ideological focus ecological

54

Ledbury, Herefordshire HR8 2TD England
Telephone 01531 670540
Electronic Mail membership@canonfromecourt.org.uk
World Wide Web http://www.canonfromecourt.org.uk

chickens, bees and Christmas geese. The huge walled garden produces year-round veg from year-round work, aided and abetted by WWOOFers. Then there is the front lawn for picnics, rounders and barbecues as well as animal grazing; a lake for "boating" and wildlife and even a swimming pool. Canon Fromers like to work, rest and play!

CENTRE FOR ALTERNATIVE TECHNOLOGY

Our community is a constituent part of the Centre for Alternative Technology which promotes and implements renewable energy, ecological building, energy efficiency, sustainable sewage treatment, permaculture and organic growing.

We twelve residents are all CAT volunteers or staff and their families. We live in either low-energy timber framed homes or eco-renovated slate quarry workers' cottages.

We are self-sufficient in drinking water filtration and reed bed sewage treatment. Our electricity is sourced from on-site wind, hydro and solar generation or "green electricity" import/export.

We have 4 communal meals a week, organise fire-wood, organic food & laundry collectively to save money, reduce our

Year started 1975
Ideological focus pragmatic

environmental impact and learn from each
other. On recent community work days we
have built a compost-loo, eco-renovated a
house, planted fruit trees
and improved our fire-
wood sheds. Decision
making is achieved
at regular commu-
nity meetings, and
is almost entirely
by consensus.
The CAT visitor
centre (excluding
our homes) is open
to day-visitors all year
round. We also host
short-term and long-term
volunteers. Applications for volunteerships
should be made by post or email with CV
to Rick Dance since we have a waiting list.

CLANABOGAN CAMPHILL COMMUNITY

The community shares life and work with adults with learning disabilities. There are six family-style house communities. Workshops include a bakery, weavery, woodworkshop. A large biodynamic farm provides milk and meat and there are fresh vegetables from the garden. A holistic life is built up with educational and cultural activities, social events and interaction with the locality. The community is Christian based, but the individual can make a free choice about participation. We are part of the international Camphill movement founded on Rudolf Stiener's anthroposophy.

Year started 1984
Ideological focus anthroposophical

15 Drudgeon Road, Clanabogan ,
Omagh, County Tyrone BT78 1TJ Northern Ireland
Fax 02882 256114
Electronic Mail camphill@btconnect.com

CLAYS LANE HOUSING CO-OPERATIVE

- -

Clays Lane Housing Co-operative is a thriving community, (we are a fully mutual co-operative), situated in London's East End. We provide accommodation for single people aged 18—65, without prejudice; we have a strong commitment to equal opportunities. New tenants are not expected to provide a deposit, and our rents are among the cheapest in London. Clays Lane was built in 1984, and consists of 107 houses arranged into ten courtyards. 57 houses are shared and purpose-built for four, six or ten people. Additionally there are 40 self-contained flats and ten self-contained bungalows, which are available to members of the co-operative through a waiting list system. Our houses are mostly ethnically mixed and some are vegetarian or vegan. We allow pets as long as it's with the agreement of other house

Year started 1977
Ideological focus co-operative

The Community Centre, Clays Lane, Stratford
London, E15 2HJ England
Telephone 020 8555 9182 **Fax** 020 8519 8696
Electronic Mail jo@clhc.org
World Wide Web http://www.clayslane.org.uk

members. Decisions are made through democratic house and courtyard meetings, as well as through elected representatives. We have a committee structure comprising a management committee and four sub-committees: membership, maintenance, equal opportunities and finance. Everyone who lives on the co-op is expected to take some part in the day-to-day running. The minimum commitment is to attend six courtyard meetings a year, and to pay your rent promptly, but the sucess of the co-operative depends on the willingness of members to join in.

THE COMMUNITY PROJECT

The Community Project is a group of people who have jointly purchased an old hospital set in 23 acres and converted it into 17 homes and 3 communal buildings. The building of 4 new detached houses is almost complete. Whilst maintaining the privacy of individual homes, the aim of the group is to live co-operatively, jointly managing the land and communal facilities, informally sharing skills and support and generally enjoying each others' company. There is no specific ideology that defines the group, however we do resemble the 'co-housing' model which is more familiar in Denmark and the US. The homes, which range from a studio flat to a five-bedroom house, were converted to suit the needs of the current members, the majority of whom are families with one or more children. Most of the 25 children

Year started 1998

Shawfield, Laughton,
Lewes, East Sussex BN8 6BY England
Telephone 01323 815733 **Fax** 01323 815702
Electronic Mail caa@brisys.demon.co.uk
World Wide Web http://www.cohousing.co.uk

attend the local primary school and many of
us are actively involved in the village community. We eat together once a week, have
monthly work days and main group meetings and regularly meet to share celebrations
and entertainment. As we are almost at the
end of our building phase we are looking at
what it means to live together, how we can
encourage an active community life without
becoming institutionalised but be much
more than simply a housing estate.

CORANI HOUSING AND LAND CO-OP

There are two adjoining Corani houses in Leicester where six to eight of us live collectively and which act as a centre for other Some People in Leicester network activities. Housing is flexible and need not be collective. There is another Leicester house and one in Stafford. Homes are mostly urban terraces at present. We work large and small allotments and we own one in Leicester which is becoming a forest garden. Capital is not essential to join but those who have it are asked to deposit some with Corani. Income pooling is expected of members and this grouping is spread equally between Leicester and the West Midlands - and includes non-Corani people. Two children have been co-parented since birth and attend school. Decision making is essentially pragmatic; by consensus where all are concerned and otherwise

Year started 1978
Ideological focus co-operative/sharing

Diggers & Dreamers 2002/03

Corani Housing and Land Co-op
12 Bartholomew Street,
Leicester, LE2 1FA England
Telephone 0116 254 5436 **Fax** 0116 255 5727
Electronic Mail democrat@devolve.org

with sensitive autonomy. We welcome, by
arrangement, visitors who will help out or
participate whilst with us. We probably have
one or two room spaces in Leicester and
Stafford for new members. Alternatively, we
have been known to accept people and
their houses! Corani is a non-equity-sharing,
fully mutual body i.e. commonwealth.

CORNERSTONE HOUSING CO-OPERATIVE

Cornerstone is not so much a community as a collective of people who share the running of a housing co-op, but who have very different perspectives, political approaches and focuses for their daily lives. Cornerstone consists of two large Victorian houses in Chapeltown, an ethnically diverse area of Leeds. Both houses need constant maintenance and have large gardens front and back where the odd co-op member does their best to create beautiful and productive landscapes. Each house has space for seven members and there are often short and long-term visitors swelling our numbers. A reasonably high turnover of members and visitors means plenty of new ideas and energy but also a pretty hectic atmosphere at times. N°16 currently also houses two dogs, two cats and a rodent sanctuary, while N°40 is animal-free. Both

Year started 1993
Ideological focus multiple/diverse

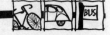

houses have office space and computer facilities. The broadly based aim of the co-operative is that members are working for social change. Other than that there is no one focus of the co-operative, but rather it provides a space where members pursue varied activities. In the past year these have included two worker co-ops (Viridian Garden Services and Footprint printers co-op), computing and web design, an anarchist book/pamphlet distribution service, prisoner support, anti GM campaigning, art college, teaching, animal rescue, peace activism, music performance, light therapy, advice work, anti fascism and supporting the local community centre, amongst others!

COVENTRY PEACE HOUSE

Following a 13-month camp outside tank manufacturer Alvis, we bought six little houses in a row as a fully mutual housing co-op and permanent peace resource for Coventry and moved in on January 21st 1999. The houses are 15 minutes (walking) from the city centre, close to a canal and opposite a scrap yard and a Hindu temple. When the renovation is finished there will be a public peace and environmental library and a large meeting space (covering the ground floor of two houses) plus co-op living space. We run a project here working with local young people not in school, training or work and they are helping with the building. There will be disabled access to all of the ground floor, plus solar panels, grey water systems etc. We also do lots of work with refugees and campaign on peace and environmental issues including

Year started 1999
Ideological focus non-violence

311 Stoney Stanton Road,
Coventry, West Midlands CV6 5DS England
Telephone 024 7666 3031
Electronic Mail covpeace@gn.apc.org
WWW http://members.gn.apc.org/~covpeacehouse

the arms trade, sanctions against Iraq and
genetic engineering. We work closely with
the local community in many ways including running courses, peace education in
schools, neighbour mediation and our own
paid work. We have a large back garden
and an allotment nearby.

We are open to new members who must be
committed to non violence and working
actively towards peace.

CRABAPPLE COMMUNITY

Crabapple's home is a slightly eccentric, crumbling Georgian house surrounded by 20 acres of beautiful woodland, pasture, orchards and vegetable, herb and flower gardens with heaps of potential and masses of thistles. All of us who live here have a deep enjoyment and love of the natural world and aspire communally to live in harmony with nature, treading as lightly on the earth as we sensibly can. Alongside our stewardship of the land we also aspire to create a safe, accessible, comfortable and happy environment in which people of all ages can grow as well as simply 'be'.

At present we're evolving suitable immediate, medium and long-term plans to take Crabapple forward with a more sustainable focus, one which, hopefully, will also involve us more in the wider community locally and

Year started 1975
Ideological focus non-ideological

globally, as well as preserving and carrying the best of the community's past into the future with us. Please write telling us a bit about yourself if you would like to visit.

CWRT Y CYLCHAU

C wrt y Cylchau, the original Welsh name meaning Court of Circles, is a five-acre smallholding situated in peaceful and beautiful hills above the Teifi river valley.

We are an all adult community of four, one of us being here in the summer months only.

Since our arrival here we have planted up a spiral orchard as the basis for a forest garden and a small mixed woodland plantation plus tree nursery beds. Our focus on permaculture is also part of a network in the wider community.

As individuals we value our own time and space and two of us have working lives outside the community. We come together to share meals, garden, care for the land and buildings and provide for guests.

We offer board and/or camping to visitors as

Year started 1998
Ideological focus ecological

a way of bringing in income and as a therapeutic retreat for those in need of healing or
just a relaxing holiday. We require prior
booking from visitors.

Our other focuses, convictions and interests
include sustainable living, cycling, walking,
hands-on-healing, psychotherapy, living
lightly, inner peace, world peace, meditation, connection with nature, spirituality,
deep ecology, wildlife and care for each
other.

DARVELL BRUDERHOF COMMUNITY

The Bruderhof is a movement of over 2500 single adults, families and older people living in eight communities in the US and Britain. Our two English communities are: Darvell Bruderhof, in Robertsbridge, East Sussex, and Beech Grove Bruderhof, in Nonington, Kent. Voluntarily pooling money, talents and energy, we base our life on the revolutionary vision and teachings of Jesus: Love each other, and your enemies. Make peace. Don't judge. Don't worry about tomorrow. We try to connect with people the world over who struggle for justice, community and the value of all life. Our children are our primary concern. Babies are cared for at the community nursery while parents work; children attend Bruderhof schools. Young adults go to local secondary schools, then are encouraged to leave the community for at least a

Year started 1920
Ideological focus christian

Darvell Bruderhof Community
Robertsbridge, East Sussex TN32 5DR England
Telephone 01580 883300 **Fax** 01580 881171
Electronic Mail info@bruderhof.com
World Wide Web http://www.bruderhof.org/

year - to live independently and make decisions about their future. Our Plough
Publishing House and our quarterly, *The
Plough* (no subscription fee) serve as tools of
dialogue. To put bread on our table, we
manufacture classroom equipment and furniture, and aids for physically disabled people. But our work is more than a business
venture: from washing laundry to assem-
bling wooden products, work is 'love made
visible'. Visitors are welcome, but are
expected to join in communal activities
and work. Please write
or phone to arrange
your stay, so that
we can
work
out
accom-
moda-
tion
details.

EQUINOX
HOUSING CO-OP

Equinox Housing Co-op was set up in 1994 and moved into a large house in inner city Manchester. Its aims were to provide affordable, quality accommodation for people involved in social change work. We are a group of 8 (plus dog) living communally and trying to build a supportive community based on the principles which we believe will help to make a better world. Our members are involved in a wide range of activities and projects including local community groups, non-violent direct action groups on many issues, ecological renovation, Manchester Environmental Resource Centre, herbalism, websites, woodlands, Radical Routes and many others. We also find time to enjoy the gardens, be sporty, play music and have (we are told) legendary parties. We have carried out extensive environmental improvements

Year started
Ideological focus eco-radical

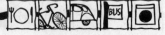

161 Hamilton Road, Longsight,
Manchester, M13 0PQ England
Telephone 0161 248 9224
Electronic Mail mail@equinox.freewire.co.uk

(rainwater toilets, insulation, community office), and are looking towards further renovations (solar heating/PV, turf roof) which will make us more sustainable. The latest development is the opportunity to buy the derelict plot next door and do a radical inner-city-permaculture-self-build-eco-house-community-workshops project. Exciting times ahead!! Visitors and helpers welcome. Membership waiting list in operation — contact us.

ISLE OF ERRAID COMMUNITY

Living on a tiny jewel of an island set into an emerald sea, our small community flourishes as we experience a sense of synchronicity with each other, our animals and the elements around us.

The heart of our community centres around our gardens as here we work hand-in-hand with nature to produce fruit and vegetables for our kitchen.

Accommodation is in our very cosy stone-built cottages heated by log-burning stoves. Although primarily vegetarian, our kitchen also offers meat supplied by our animals.

Our membership is quite small, only eight adults and one child, but there is always something going on, be it walks, boat trips, singalongs etc.

Year started 1975
Ideological focus sustainable

Isle of Erraid Community, Findhorn Foundation, Fionnphort,
Isle Of Mull, Argyll PA66 6BN Scotland
Telephone 01681 700384
Electronic Mail paul@unicorn3.demon.co.uk
World Wide Web http://www.erraid.freeserve.co.uk

Our island community also opens its doors
to guests who stay with us for anything
ranging from one week to a couple of years.
Meditation and singing play a part in our
lives as we meet daily to pursue both.
For further information, please contact us.

FINDHORN FOUNDATION

The only thing that stays the same at Findhorn, is change. People come here and experience inner changes: their hearts opening, their minds relaxing, their consciousness expanding. The community itself is always changing too: new management structures, new decision-making procedures, new initiatives moving forward - all the better to reflect the deeper issues and possible solutions of our times. After 38 years Findhorn is still committed to serving spirit, with "work is love in action" still being the most widely practised mode of service; it's just that the kinds of work keep changing and developing over the years. Where once the Findhorn Foundation was known as the place where people talked to nature spirits and grew 40-pound cabbages, it is now known for its community, its educational activities, and its develop-

Year started 1962
Ideological focus celebrating the divinity in all of life

Findhorn Foundation, The Park, Findhorn,
Forres, Morayshire IV36 3TZ Scotland
Telephone 01309 690311
Electronic Mail reception@findhorn.org
World Wide Web http://www.findhorn.org

ing eco-village (and some of us still do com-
municate directly with nature). All of these
activities are the natural continuation of ear-
lier work done in these areas. People from
all over the world come to Findhorn for
Experience Weeks and other courses, and
many find inspiration to bring spirit more
present in their everyday lives. The community has its own gardens, kitchens, businesses, sanctuaries and various buildings, and
welcomes guests all year round.

FIRESIDE HOUSING CO-OP

Fireside is situated in the inner city of Sheffield. We are very lucky to live in an area where there is plenty of green space, our four adjacent terraced houses back onto a lovely old cemetery and there's an adventure playground at the end of the road. We share a large garden, in which there is plenty of space for the children from the co-op and their friends to play, space to grow our organic veg and ample space for fires and parties too. We have plans to build a children's playhouse in the garden this summer too. We have a wind generator and a solar panel which we use as a display at local festivals. We are interested in renewable energies on a national scale as well as small design projects at home. Each house is

Year started 1996

run as a separate household, so we have a
lot of personal space. We do, however, eat
communally on a regular basis, particularly
when having a workday on the houses or
gardens.

FOX HOUSING CO-OP

We live on our co-operatively owned 70-acre farm with agro-forestry orchards, willow beds, woodland planting. Also, 17 acres of organic vegetables and a large box scheme provide us with enough to live simply whilst funding other projects here i.e. hostel space, events field.

Our first years have revolved around making a foundation for our community - financially and emotionally. Also reaffirming our focus - taking responsibility for ourselves in as many ways as possible, i.e. ecological living, vegan eating, personal growth, supporting freedom from addictions, seeking spirituality in the land around us. This year we're renovating outbuildings into eco-homes (alternative technology /wheelchair access). Also planning the next adventure - creating an eco-village and having more kids here.

Year started 1998
Ideological focus ecological

Werndolau, Gelli Aur,
Carmarthen, Dyfed SA32 8NE Wales
Telephone 01558 668798 **Fax** 01558 668088
Electronic Mail foxers@ukonline.co.uk
World Wide Web http://www.rawgem.co.uk/fox

We work hard, like clear structure and
communication — we have rotas and weekly
meetings, making decisions by consensus.
We play together and have "quiet weekends" where we spend quality time having
fun. We eat well and together too!
We welcome visitors who come to help out,
and have several paid opportunities to live
in community for a year and work on the
box scheme. Drop us a line if you're interested ...

FRANKLEIGH HOUSE COMMUNITY

Frankleigh House was bought at auction by one family for £285,000 in 1995. A deposit of £28,500 was paid using money from intending residents. During the 28 days before legal completion 4 more families joined as equal shareholders in the newly formed company. Triodos bank came to the rescue the day after the auction and made a formal offer of £190,000 in 10 days, enabling the purchase to be completed. The building is now worth over £2M, the 8 families in residence have split into 2 groups. This may result in the property being split or some other creative solution. There is plenty of room for more members to enjoy the huge Victorian mansion and out-buildings, 17 acres, tennis court and swimming pool. Residents work from home and outside as musicians, property developers, computer consultants, health practitioners etc. People

Year started 1995
Ideological focus cohousing

Frankleigh House, Bath Road,
Bradford-on-Avon, Wiltshire BA15 2PB England
Telephone 01225 866467
Electronic Mail info@frankleigh.com
World Wide Web http://www.frankleigh.com

enjoy hanging out a lot, drinking coffee, all
in a beautiful setting - 20 minutes walk from
Bradford on Avon. Some children are
home-educated. At the moment members
have to buy in to join and we are all equal
shareholders with decision making by consensus — things look like they will change!
Check out the web site for updates on how
to join.

GAUNTS HOUSE
COMMUNITY

The community at Gaunts House is informal and more inevitable than intentional. We are a community dedicated to providing a space for others to come and learn more about themselves and life. Our structure includes employed staff, members, guests, students, trainees and volunteers. Our purpose is to seek, find and follow our individually right paths, and to provide care and support for others.

We welcome people of all ages to join us short and long-term. Ideally you would be committed to profound learning and service, to seeking and following your own path. Young people, aged 17 to 29 can come on an energy exchange basis for a minimum of one month, up to six months. More mature adults can come as a paying Resident Guest initially. After a period of time you may be able to join the community on a regular

Year started 1990

Gaunts House Community
Wimborne, Dorset BH21 4JQ England
Telephone 01202 841522 **Fax** 01202 841959
Electronic Mail admin@rgf-gaunts.demon.co.uk
World Wide Web http://www.rgf-gaunts.demon.co.uk

energy exchange basis. There are also
arrangements for locals to join in as volunteers, and for committed volunteers - friends
from the area and further afield, who commit to regular volunteering arrangements.
We run regular Community Experience
Weekends to give a taste of our lives and
ways. This is the ideal opportunity to find
out if our community is right for you.

GLANEIRW HOUSING CO-OP

laneirw is a small farm in West Wales with 44 acres of land. We live in a large shabby house and a cottage. We try to get most of our food from the land, there is a walled garden, an orchard, a market garden field and polytunnels for fruit and vegetable growing. We keep pigs, chickens and ducks. The 5 acres of mature broadleaf woodland has 12 acres of mixed broadleaf added over the years and the ash and willow is for our eventual fuel supply. There is a mortgage to pay so there is a business repairing, converting and supplying parts for Rayburn cookers and a pottery workshop with our own shop. We pool our income and take weekly pocket money. Everyone has their own room but other rooms are communal. We share a meal every evening and have informal meetings every week. Housework, cooking

Year started 1975
Ideological focus ecological /emotional

Diggers & Dreamers 2002/03

and emptying the compost toilets, are also shared. New ventures for the year are bee keeping, digging a drainage ditch, new pottery and shop and separating the kitchen from the lounge. We enjoy having visitors but please write and make arrangements first. We are particularly interested in diggers and weeders, builders and alternative energy experts, but anyone with energy and humour is welcome. Please no dogs or cats and no park-ups.

GLYN ABBEY

W e live in an old country estate of 10 acres. There are nine shares (the last share to change hands was 6 years ago). We have 9 separate households with 9 distinct dwellings, some still in the process of being 'reclaimed'. There are compost toilets, spring water, separate organic gardens (mainly), no management structure, no agreed ideology. Current age range is 9 to 60. The 17 adults including teachers, social workers, labourers, caterering staff, scientists, office and shop workers, horticulturalists, artists and artisans, writers, performers and musicians; some gainfully employed in the outside world and some not. Eight children are educated locally. Six 'ex-children' (over 18) return regularly from other parts. There are also two dogs, assorted cats and a few chickens. We come together officially twice per year,

Year started 1976
Ideological focus ecological

●●●●●●●●●●●●●●●●●●●●●●●●●●●●●●●●●●●●●

at New Year and for our Mayfair, everything else is ad hoc. Some of us would like to learn how to structure meetings or community business, in such a way that conflict or fear of conflict would not sabotage them; as we have no business meetings and no structure for such. Some of us would also like to offer places for WOOFERS and WOROODS (workers on restoration of old derelicts)!

THE GRAIL COMMUNITY

The Grail community is one of several branches of the Grail Society which started in Holland in 1921. It is a Roman Catholic institute of single and married people. The society seeks, in an increasingly impersonal world, to promote understanding of the uniqueness and value of each person. The long-term community at Waxwell consists of single women who make a life commitment, sharing resources and observing accountability to the group. Waxwell is a listed Elizabethan house with conference extensions, set in ten acres of wooded garden. The work consists of supporting families and married people, publishing, hospitality, and workshops on arts, spirituality, stress management and the provision of space and solitude. Short-term members and volunteers are welcome. The former share our life for a year and partici-

Year started 1932
Ideological focus christian

pate in the work of the community whilst
exploring new directions. Volunteers, many
from overseas, live alongside the community
helping with the running of the house and
upkeep of the grounds. On a daily basis,
people come for activities such as weaving,
spinning, study and prayer groups, healing,
relaxation and yoga. Believers of all traditions and of none are welcome. New devel-
opments in our leadership structures have
prompted us to draw more readily on the
generous help and expertise of our members, contacts and friends throughout the
country, many of whom are frequent visitors.

GRIMSTONE COMMUNITY

Grimstone Manor is set in 27 acres of garden, pasture and wilderness on the edge of Dartmoor. The Community's main focus is to create and maintain a supportive space for a wide range of personal development groups who visit us throughout the year. We try to run our business with integrity, balancing its needs with that of the group participants, ourselves and the environment. We meet weekly, making decisions by consensus. All members share some of the core work as well as specializing in areas of particular interest. Work is paid at a common hourly rate. Our future development is a continual topic for discussion and we are open to suggestions for new ventures regarding the community itself and the groups that we welcome here. In the past two years we

Year started 1990
Ideological focus eco-spiritual

Grimstone Manor, Horrabridge,
Yelverton, Devon PL20 7QY England
Telephone 01822 854358 **Fax** 01822 852318
Electronic Mail enquiries@grimstonemanor.co.uk
World Wide Web http://www.grimstonemanor.co.uk

have initiated and run the local community
composting scheme and individual members have been involved in diverse projects
ranging from the
formation of an
eco-psychology
network to a
monthly acoustic
music cafe. We
are open to
enquires from
long- and short-
term volunteers,
WWOOFers and
possible new
members with
energy, skills, and
in the case of the
members, capital,

who are keen to join us in this caring, supportive and beautiful space to live and grow.

GWERIN HOUSING ASSOCIATION

Gwerin is a community of five houses, four of which are part of a Victorian terrace. These large houses are shared between members of the Association. Each house is run differently, according to the individuals who live there. We have weekly meetings where the whole membership comes together to discuss the running of the Association. We are a mixture of individuals, and as a community have no particular ideological focus. Gwerin now holds five properties. We operate on a small budget produced by rents, and the labour of all members in renovation of the properties and supporting the decisions of the weekly group meetings. Every aspect of the Association is open to scrutiny by all members who, in turn, volunteer their skills to ensure that the rules of the constitution are tempered by the day-to-day reality of

Year started 1977
Ideological focus consensual co-operative

Gwerin Housing Association
121 Hagley Road, Old Swinford,
Stourbridge, West Midlands DY8 1RD England
Electronic Mail Gwerin@discordian.co.uk

life in the Community. Gwerin also strives to support adults with special needs, in a Community atmosphere, using our strong ties with Dudley Social Services. The Coachouse Project is now well established, in partnership with St.Mary's Church, with Gwerin members situated in the Cottage overseeing a workshop at the Coachouse, offering various arts/crafts activities at cost to the local community.

HEARTWOOD COMMUNITY

We are a Housing Co-op located on a 35-acre farm six miles south of Carmarthen. The land has eight acres of beautiful oak and ash woodland with streams running through it, 13 acres of good quality pasture and some unimproved land. We intend to plant trees, create a Forest Garden and wildflower meadow, as well as developing more areas for growing food. There is currently a three-bedroom house with planning permission for an extension, and some outbuildings which we plan to convert using eco-friendly methods. We intend to create further individual and family units and large areas for community use. We are a group of people who have a background in personal growth and work with people - counselling, mediation, youth-

Year started 1997
Ideological focus eco-spiritual

Diggers & Dreamers 2002/03

Heartwood Community
Blaen Y Wern, Llangyndeyrne,
Kidwelly, Sir Gaerfyrddin SA17 5ES Wales
Electronic Mail Becky@heartwood.freeserve.co.uk

work, management consultancy and teaching. We have lived together since 1997, spending two years looking for our farm, and have spent much time nurturing our personal relationships. The core of our community rests on how we develop and sustain our relationships and our practise of Permaculture includes sustainable relationships with each other as well as with the land we live on. We share rituals and life events together in a way that is meaningful, spiritual and respectful. We make plans with the generations to come in mind, through conscious decisions about how we use the land, materials and the earth's resources. We share incomes, car(s), meals, a washing machine and lots of trust! We are currently looking for other people, who share our values.

THE HIVE
HOUSING CO-OP

The Hive are from a diverse range of tendencies (anarchist, socialist, suicidal....) united by a shared belief in social change through grassroots action (solidarity campaigns, housing and human rights, community food growing and catering....) and of course co-operation. We reached a limit of tolerance of squalid living conditions and naughty landlords that dominate the Bradford property scene. So we decided to own our own squalid living conditions, in a friendly sustainable DIY manner.

In June 1997, having secured an Ecology Building Society mortgage and a Radical Routes loan, we dived into a brilliant but sadly neglected four storey terrace house in sunny Manningham. At a steady pace we

Year started 1997
Ideological focus dreamers

16 Spring Gardens,
Bradford, West Yorkshire BD1 3EJ England
Electronic Mail the_hive_coop@yahoo.com
WWW http://www.geocities.com/the_hive_coop

waddled towards many of original aspirations, whilst revising others. These include: a reasonable bit of DIY repair and renewal; the development of a nice wee garden cum scrapyard; the establishment of a street association and community garden; playing an active role in Radical Routes; and a bicycle breeding programme that's seen us chasing off Raleigh corporate spies. Just around the corner are our more daring dreams: serious eco-renovation, unilateral declaration of independence, and a permanently tidy hallway.

HOCKERTON
HOUSING PROJECT

The Hockerton Housing Project (HHP) is the UK's first earth sheltered, self-sufficient ecological housing development. The residents of the five houses generate their own clean energy, harvest their own water and recycle waste materials causing minimal pollution or carbon dioxide emissions. The houses are amongst the most energy efficient, purpose-built dwellings in Europe. The houses are the focus of a holistic way of living, which combines the production of organic foods, low intensity fish farming, promotion of wildlife and the planting of thousands of trees.

The project was conceived in the early 1990s. It took two years to complete the planning agreement with the local authority and a further two years to build the homes and facilities.

Over the years the project has established

Year started 1995
Ideological focus none

The Watershed, Gables Drive, Hockerton
Southwell, Nottinghamshire NG25 0QU
Telephone 01636 816902
Electronic Mail hhp@hockerton.demon.co.uk
World Wide Web http://www.hockerton.demon.co.uk

itself as an exemplar of sustainable development. As a result of this it has developed a range of services through the creation of a small on-site business. This workers' co-operative provides a level of employment for its members, whilst promoting sustainable development. Its activities include running guided tours, workshops, talks, consultancy and, soon to be launched, a match-making service. (see p 219)
Although each family has their own home, the community share food growing, site maintenance, managing the facilities and a common sustainable business.

HOLY ROOD HOUSE

One of the county's hidden gems - a place of peace, tranquility and contentment - is to be found nestling beneath the shadow of the Hambleton hills at Sowerby, the old part of the bustling market town of Thirsk, made famous by the James Herriot books and their television off-shoots.

Just journey through the ancient market square following the route of the old A1, branching off by the fishing tackle shop on your left by the roundabout and within minutes you are there outside the imposing building that is Holy Rood House.

Before 1993, this house was home to the Order of the Sisters of the Holy Rood, but since the nuns left in 1992 it has been the Centre for Health and Pastoral Care, retaining the name of the Order and welcoming men and women from all over the country,

Year started 1994
Ideological focus christian

10 Sowerby Road, Sowerby,
Thirsk, North Yorkshire YO7 1HX England
Telephone 01845 522580 **Fax** 01845 527300
Electronic Mail holyroodhouse@centrethirsk.fsnet.co.uk
World Wide Web http://www.holyroodhouse.freeuk.com

irrespective of their personal belief.
Holy Rood is now a place where everyone
can sit and relax and enjoy delicious home
made food. They may like to explore their
artistic side in the art and pottery room, try
their hand at drama or weaving, or find further peace and relaxation with yoga or body
massage with aromatherapy.
If anyone has anything on their minds, then
they are able to talk in complete confidence
to one of the many fully qualified counsel-
lors who make themselves available.
Whatever your reason for
visiting Holy Rood, you
are assured of a
warm and
friendly
wel-
come.

KEVERAL FARM COMMUNITY

Keveral Farm is 30 acres of veggie plots, woodland, orchard, pasture and wilderness, certified organic with the Soil Association. Some community members live in the farmhouse, others in caravans and benders. There is a visitor's barn for courses and workshops and tipis for quiet space. Our course programme is expanding; along with our annual perma-culture design course. We have a peaceful, leafy camping area set amongst our orchard, popular with visitors in the summer months for holidays and small events. We are 10 minutes walk through the woods from the sea. We operate as a co-op and purchased Keveral in 1997 using loans from Triodos Bank and Radical Routes, after renting it for 23 years. The house is owned and managed by our housing co-op (One Community) and the farm is managed by our workers co-op (Keveral Farmers). The members of the community manage both co-ops. We are

Year started 1973

very work focused, our main activity being a
veggie box scheme supplying 160 local
households. There are a number of other
projects, including mushrooms, 'Wild Magic'
liquid plant feed, soft fruit and preserves,
and woodland work. We will soon start
pressing apples for juice and cider. These
projects provide about half of Keveral's
members with a basic income, other members claim income support, make and sell
crafts, or work locally. We welcome
WWOOFers and other working visitors.
Please write for further information about
visiting, saying a bit about yourself and
enclose an SAE. Sorry, we cannot take
everyone who writes.

LAURIESTON HALL

Twenty-eight of us, aged four to seventy-one, with occasional long-suffering, long-staying visitors, and currently two prospective new residents (one in utero) live in this rambling pink pile built around a sixteenth century fortified tower house. We co-operatively manage 135 acres of surrounding woodland, pasture and marsh, including the small corner of a loch (normally brass monkeys to tepid, occasionally gorgeous).

We live semi-communally, wandering into the woods each week to collect the couple of tons of timber needed for the wood-stoves; growing fruit and veg on a prodigious scale; allowing hens, pigs, cows and bees to keep us busy; doing our own maintenance, keeping the hydro-electric plant going and indulging at times in bouts of talking, listening, playing and performing.

Year started 1972
Ideological focus elusive

Visitors come on Maintenance Weeks (usually April, July and September) to help us with the construction, gardening, land work and domestics. We also offer a full programme of week-long events: music, self-help, creative, lesbian and gay etc. Please send an A4-sized SAE (44p) for the newsletter.

It would be wrong to say we have no ideological focus, but we prefer that it be elusive. We trust in each other to take as much control, individually and co-operatively, over our lives as we can. We believe in compost, laughing, wellies and freedom. OK, maybe we can talk about the last one.

LEE ABBEY ASTON HOUSEHOLD COMMUNITY

We are a small ecumenical Christian community of adults, part of the wider Lee Abbey Fellowship, committed to living and working in a multi-faith, multi-racial area. Our Victorian terraced house has four single and one double bedrooms, a community lounge, kitchen and bathroom all upstairs. Downstairs has facilities which can be used by others in the neighbourhood for committee meetings, quiet days etc, with a pleasant garden.

We meet together for prayer around the breakfast table, and eat our evening meal together, often with other 'friends of the community' joining us. We share the tasks of shopping, cleaning, cooking and entertaining, and pool our wages or benefits, receiving a weekly amount for personal use. We have a community car, but two of us cycle

Year started 1988
Ideological focus christian

Lee Abbey Aston Household Community
121 Albert Road, Aston,
Birmingham, West Midlands B6 5ND England
Telephone 0121 326 8280

whenever possible. We try to reach decisions by consensus, when we remember, and are committed to spending time together, supporting, encouraging and listening to each other. We do paid or voluntary work, spend time with local folk, offer hospitality, and share our faith as and when appropriate. Each of us is an active member of a local fellowship or church, and we want to deepen our faith. We offer a supportive, reflective, prayerful environment in which to experience life in the inner city. Enquiries welcome.

LITTLE GROVE COMMUNITY

L ittle Grove was established in 1983. We are broadly "alternative" in outlook and values. We are all pretty actively involved in the world, with a wide variety of jobs. Some of us work partly or wholly from home. There are 5 acres of gardens and fields. Some main meals are eaten together. House business meetings are held fortnightly and there is a monthly meeting to deal with other matters. Little Grove is in a very quiet rural setting, but close to several towns and about an hour from London. We are working on changing our existing structure, in which each member has a room or two of their own with shared bathrooms and kitchens to a co-housing community consisting of individual units with their own kitchens and bathrooms. This will involve developing some of our existing buildings into individual units and maybe

Year started 1983

Little Grove Community
Grove Lane,
Chesham, Buckinghamshire HP5 3QQ England
Telephone 01494 778080

some new-build. We aim to do all this to
high ecological standards. Communal
spaces for cooking, eating, meeting, working and relaxing will continue to be an
important part of our lives. Individual workspaces will be available. We shall remain a
housing co-operative, but there will be
changes to our legal structure.
Please send a 38p stamp for details.

LOSANG DRAGPA
BUDDHIST CENTRE

Losang Dragpa Centre is a Buddhist college and retreat centre which provides a place where people can learn about the Buddhist way of life. We offer working holidays throughout the year. In return for 35 hours per week (decorating, gardening, cleaning and building work) we provide food, accommodation and teachings.

Year started 1985
Ideological focus buddhist

Dobroyd Castle, Pexwood Road,
Todmorden, West Yorkshire OL14 7JJ England
Telephone 01706 812247 **Fax** 01706 818901
Electronic Mail info@losangdragpa.com
World Wide Web http://www.losangdragpa.com

LOTHLORIEN COMMUNITY

Lothlorien is a therapeutic community for people with mental health problems. We have links with Samye Ling Tibetan Centre in Dumfriesshire. Buddhist values of compassion and tolerance are the basis of our approach, but we are not a religious community and we are open to everyone. The community consists of 8 people with mental health problems and 4 voluntary co-workers, living in a large log house on 17 acres of land. The 3 staff, who provide a continuity of support to the community, are non resident. We have a strong belief in everyone's potential for well being, even in the midst of pain and distress. We believe that people need not be imprisoned by their past. We aim to help people to develop their strengths and work towards recovery through the shared experience of community life. We avoid diagnosing or

Year started 1978
Ideological focus buddhist

Corsock, Castle Douglas, Kirkudbrightshire.
Dumfries & Galloway DG7 3DR Scotland
Telephone 01644 440602
WWW: http://www.lothlorien.tc

labelling, and attempt to break down the
distinction which frequently exists between
those seen as 'well' and those seen as
'unwell'. The ordinary practical tasks of community life, such as gardening, cooking and
cleaning have a grounding effect, and the
rhythm of daily life provides a structure
which helps to restore a sense of balance to
people's lives. Central to the life of the community is the daily meeting, where we plan
work and other activities, make decisions
and attempt to address issues of living
together as a group in an open way.
Lothlorien has vacancies on a regular basis,
as the maximum stay is two years.

MADHYAMAKA CENTRE

Madhyamaka Centre's primary function is to introduce and promote the teachings of Buddha. Central to Buddhist teaching is that happiness and unhappiness depend upon the mind, and by using the tool of meditation we can learn to develop a deep inner peace and contentment.

Based in a Georgian Mansion 15 miles from York, Madhyamaka Centre welcomes around 2000 visitors each year. The Centre runs regular Day and Weekend Courses which introduce the basic techniques of meditation. A popular way of visiting the Centre free of charge is through our 'Working Holiday Weeks'. In exchange for 35 hours voluntary work, we provide full board and accomodation for 7 nights with

Year started 1986
Ideological focus buddhist

Kilnwick Percy Hall, Kilnwick Percy, Pocklington
York, Yorkshire YO42 1UF England
Telephone 01759 304832 **Fax** 01759 305962
Electronic Mail info@madhyamaka.org
World Wide Web http://www.madhyamaka.org

•••••••••••••••••••••••••••

an option to attend Evening Classes during
term time. The work varies but may include
working in our grounds, cooking or cleaning
etc.

Visitors are requested not to smoke or drink
in the Centre.

MONIMAIL TOWER PROJECT

●●●●●●●●●●●●●●●●●●●●●●●●●●●●●●●

Monimail Tower is the only remains of Cardinal Beaton's Palace built in the 16th century. In 1985 a community was started on the land around the Tower. Most of the land is woodland. There is also a large orchard and walled garden. We live in a Segal self-build house and also in rooms in the Tower itself. We are legally constituted as an educational charity promoting learning in the field of organic horticulture, and also aiming to benefit disadvantaged people. We try to share as much as possible from food and work to skills and resources. We eat a mostly vegetarian diet, organic if possible. The main areas of responsibility are the garden, the woods, building and maintenance and administration. We pay rent to the Project and do not share income. We would like to find more ways of becoming self supporting.

Year started 1985

Monimail Tower Project
Letham, Monimail
by Cupar, Fife KY15 7RJ Scotland

We
also
like
to
meet
people, play music,
dance and gener-
ally have fun.
We have regu-
lar meetings
and make
our deci-
sions by
consensus. Our
aim is to develop a resource for ourselves
and other people with which to learn how
to live together in a way that is beneficial to
all. We are open to people from whatever
background to visit and take part. For more
information please write enclosing a
stamped addressed envelope.

MONKTON WYLD COURT

●●●●●●●●●●●●●●●●●●●●●●●●●●●●●●●●●

Monkton Wyld Court is a holistic education centre run by a community of 12-16 adults plus children and cats. The setting is a neo-gothic Victorian rectory and outbuildings placed in a beautiful Dorset valley three miles from the sea at Lyme Regis. There are 11 acres of grounds which comprise a small farm, a one-acre walled organic vegetable garden, terraced lawns, children's play area, woods and a stream. The house sleeps up to 35 guests and includes two large group rooms, a piano room, library, meditation hut, healing room, craft shop, pottery and arts facilities. We try to maintain a balance between being a community and running a business. As a community, we work, eat, sing and sometimes play together. Each morning we come together to 'attune' and plan the day. Domestic work is done by rota. Decision-

Year started 1982
Ideological focus sustainable living

Monkton Wyld Court, Charmouth,
Bridport, Dorset DT6 6DQ England
Telephone 01297 560342 **Fax** 01297 560395
Electronic Mail monktonwyldcourt@btinternet.com
World Wide Web http://www.monkton.btinternet.co.uk

making is moving towards a form of consensus. Joining Monkton Wyld is also a full-time commitment. Our income is generated through a year-round programme of courses and private bookings, plus B&B. We also run a kindergarten for the local community. The contribution made by short-term volunteers and WWOOFers is vital, both in terms of work and fresh energy. Volunteering is also the way in for potential new residents, but you need to book early!

"The Road to Monkton"

MORNINGTON GROVE COMMUNITY

We are a community of fourteen diverse people (of all ages, heterosexual and gay) otherwise united by loosely libertarian, green, feminist and spiritual ideals. We live in two beautiful adjoining Victorian houses with a large garden, in a densely populated part of East London. We originated as an offshoot of another London community, Some Friends. We organise mainly through fortnightly meetings, where decisions are taken by consensus. These alternate between business and social meetings Each household is responsible for its own day-to-day practicalities. We have a unique economic system. Each year we estimate our forthcoming annual expenditure, dividing this by the number of members to give an average 'rent'. Each of us then decides what we can indiviually afford. If these amounts meet the total,

Year started 1982
Ideological focus indefinable

••

wonderful; if not, we rethink our personal
contributions until our projected costs are
met. To give some idea of our interests, our
current occupations involve carpentry, computing, editing, design, environmental
activism, homeopathy, massage, museum
work, parenting, performance, psychotherapy,
teaching, temping and reflexology. We
describe ourselves as a vegetarian, non-
smoking community (but one or two of us
do eat meat or smoke elsewhere).

THE NEIGHBOURS

The Neighbours Community is an ecumenical Christian community of households, living in five adjacent terraced houses in a suburban road in Northampton. We have been here since 1984. Each household has its own living space and, in addition, there are some communal rooms and a large garden common to all. There are nine adults living in the Community and seven school-age children. Members earn their living outside the Community and include a physiotherapist, manager of the local soup kitchen, a doctor in general practice and three retired people. Members contribute to a Common Fund for shared expenses. Our purpose is to develop a community life which enables us to explore and share our faith and care for others according to the Gospel. Our wider aims are to encourage Christian unity and com-

Year started 1984
Ideological focus christian

The Neighbours Community
140-148 Ardington Road,
Northampton, NN1 5LT England
Telephone 01604 633918
Electronic Mail neighbours@totalise.co.uk

munity and to seek understanding with those of other faiths. Members are active in several local church congregations including Church of England, Roman Catholic, and Religious Society of Friends (Quakers). We meet for prayers every morning and for meals together several times a week. We have a programme of events to which we invite people from outside the Community. These include quiet days, creativity days, Taizé prayer, children's events, agapé suppers. In March 2001 we ran a two-day workshop on 'Spirituality and Breadmaking'. The Neighbours is intended to be the sort of community which can happen anywhere.

NEW EDUCATION HOUSING CO-OP

Formerly part of Common Ground in Birmingham, the co-op relocated in July 2000 and purchased a four/five bedroomed house (built circa 1918) with a long garden, 15 miles north of Swansea (40 minutes by bus) in the upper Swansea valley. The location was chosen for its mountain views and walks and its accessibility by public transport to the outstanding beauty of the Brecon Beacons and the Gower Peninsula coastline.

We share housework and bills, food is bought collectively and evening meals are eaten together. Electrical appliances are few (no television, fridge, washing machine). We promote and practically apply drug-free, tobacco-free and alcohol-free living. Co-op meetings are weekly, more often if it is necessary to meet a specific deadline. Our longest-standing member joined in 1990

Year started 1986

and our newest member in 1997 (having come to permanent co-ops in the 1980s and short-life housing co-ops in the 1990s). We are specifically concerned with: instantaneous and complete radical change in individuals; radical health promotion; vegan issues; growing food vegan/organically; collectively owning resources; home education; liberated parenting; living lightly. Visitors are charged only for food and baths. Please enclose an A5 sae when first writing to us.

OLD HALL COMMUNITY

•••••••••••••••••••••••••••••••••

The richness of our maturing community is echoed by the shouts and laughter from grandchildren and we are frequently asked what is the formula for our success? In reality ours is neither success nor failure. We prefer to be non-competitive; we find there is a unity through diversity for those who live here; we eat together and grow our food together, taking pride in its organic production. Yet each can escape to their own private space in the large rambling house when there is the need. Traditions have established themselves, marking the seasons, honouring the times of the year — Easter egg hunt, maypole dancing, potato harvest, Halloween, and the end-of-year pantomime which, by rewriting a traditional storyboard, enables us to make fun and laugh at ourselves.

Over the years we have developed our facil-

Year started 1974
Ideological focus ecological

Old Hall Community
Rectory Hill, East Bergholt,
Colchester, Essex CO7 6TG England
Telephone 01206 298294
Electronic Mail mcgain@btinternet.com

...ities so that they may be used by outside organisations like IVS and Peace Brigade International. Our extended family of friends has become truly international with volunteer workers from as far away as Hungary, Sweden, Italy and Spain. Our family in residence ranges from aged three to eighty years.

Thoughts toward a more sustainable way of living now move us into the next phase. We are in the process of a major solar panel installation to supply hot water, once again demonstrating commitment with almost all the work being undertaken in house.

Please write in the first instance to the Applicant Secretary.

PARKDALE YOGA CENTRE

The Parkdale Yoga Centre is a small urban commune dedicated to living simply and well. We have a peaceful Victorian house in a pleasant setting in Wolverhampton. Our activities include practising and teaching Yoga (in all its aspects), giving Shiatsu treatments, and tending two organic allotments.

At the moment we are three members and are seeking one or two more people to share the fun and the work of this project with. Visitors interested in what we are doing are welcome, especially if they want to learn Yoga, organic growing, or about holistic living in a non-sectarian context. They must, however, be able to fend for themselves sometimes, since we are often very busy!

Philosophically, we value humour and the simplicity of ordinary life as the means of

Year started 1996
Ideological focus tolerant yoga - ecological

side-stepping the alienation of mainstream
culture. We believe in being linked with the
community we are embedded in even
whilst we politely refuse its dominant culture - hence the classes and complementary
health treatments, the work contribution
and other help we accept from our friends.
It is possible to live well now. (You may miss
the chance if you wait for the revolution!)
Amongst other things, it involves the work,
however modest in scale, of creating the
conditions for alternatives to the mainstream to grow.

PARSONAGE FARM

Parsonage Farm is a community of nine adults and five children about 12 miles from Cambridge. We live in a large old house in 3.5 acres of land at the edge of a large village. Most people have absorbing jobs outside the community so the main activity that brings us together is caring for the large organic vegetable garden that supplies most of our vegetarian diet (with occasional fish!). Every third weekend or so we work together with WWOOFers on the garden and we commit ourselves to one week a year of house maintenance. The community has a large Elizabethan barn where there is workshop space and the potential for development of other ideas. We eat together in the evening and support each other informally in childcare and life. Some people here work in Delta T Devices

Year started 1971

(formed by community members 20 years ago), a co-op business producing electronic research instruments. We are a varied group with interests ranging from re-evaluating counselling to gardening, macrobiotic cooking and music and dance. We like to relax together, particularly in the summer, when barbecues and trips to swim in a local brick pit (and cover ourselves in clay!) are regular features. Our group has been going through a lot of change recently and for the first time for many years we may look for new members. At the moment, tho, we are having a breathing space to take stock and decide where we want to go as a group. We are open to people coming for a weekend visit to garden with us through the WWOOF organisation.

PENNINE CAMPHILL COMMUNITY

Our main area of work is supporting a college for students with learning disabilities. We're quite a mixed bunch, some who have lived here for twenty years and some who come just for a year to help out. There's always quite an international flavour within the community which we encourage. Co-workers living in the community have their everyday needs met but don t receive a wage. There are also others working at Pennine but living locally. Our farm, garden and traditional craft workshops create unique 'hands-on' learning for our students. We are also home to Wakefield Riding for the Disabled, a project we have run jointly for over ten years. We also have two unemployment projects running.

Year started 1977
Ideological focus anthroposophy

Boyne Hill, Chapelthorpe,
Wakefield, West Yorkshire WF4 3JH England
Telephone 01924 255281 **Fax** 01924 240257
Electronic Mail enquiries@pennine.org.uk
World Wide Web http://www.pennine.org.uk

Most of our students are residential and
share our houses on an extended family
basis.
We would like to grow (so much to do) and
welcome people and ideas. Get in touch!

PEOPLE IN COMMON

•••••••••••••••••••••••••••••••••••

PIC was originally in a number of terraced houses in Burnley. The community moved into the mill 12 years ago, when the area was predominantly rural, with a couple of small industrial estates nearby. The mill sits on four acres of riverside land (the Lancashire Calder). We have created a variety of different areas, from wild and woody, to highly cultivated. The site has become a green oasis in the midst of a growing number of steadily expanding industrial estates/business parks. We are currently low in numbers and are considering several different options for future development, in Altham, or maybe elsewhere. Between us we have interests in gardening, cooking, Cuba solidarity, films, fiction, tadpoles and newts, mental health issues, basketry, wwwebweaving, music (from metal to Mozart), history: human and natural,

Year started 1974
Ideological focus left

red/green politics, photography, drawing, and dominoes. We don't have pets and only allow smoking in a limited part of the building. If you are mature, down-to-earth, with practical skills/interests, left leaning, feminist, good humoured and have clear boundaries with children, if you are looking for a community to join, check us out.

PILSDON COMMUNITY

The Pilsdon Community was started 40 years ago in this 17th century manor house in a remote part of Dorset. Since then it has welcomed thousands to find a home here, some returning year after year. Guests come from all walks of life and are usually facing some sort of crisis — homelessness, breakdown, addictions etc. We aim for as normal and homely an atmosphere as possible in which guests can take their time to sort out their next step. We do not set an initial limit to a person's stay. We also offer two free nights to wayfarers passing through. A smallholding of 9 acres with various animals and a large vegetable garden involve guests in sharing in the care and maintenance — always a hoover, spade, paintbrush or hammer at work somewhere! But everyone gets drawn in to muck out the cows' winter quarters! Six (currently) core

Year started 1958
Ideological focus christian

Pilsdon Manor, Bridport, Dorset DT2 9QS England
Telephone 01308 868308 **Fax** 01308 868161
Electronic Mail pilsdon@lineone.com
World Wide Web http://website.lineone.net/~pilsdon

"members" plus their families (and occasional other volunteers) live in and have responsibility for the Community (not salaried but supported). We share broadly in a Christian spirituality, participate in daily prayer/meditation and enjoy the privilege of offering hospitality. We are often remembered for our good food! (However, we are by necessity strictly alcohol-free).

PLANTS FOR A FUTURE

We are a registered charity carrying out research into edible and otherwise useful plants, sustainable, vegan, organic horticulture and the dissemination of information about these topics. We are currently in the process of making a planning application for our new site in Devon and moving our base.

Plants for a Future consists of two fundamental groups, the charity and the workers' co-op. The workers' co-op looks after the land and carries out the practicalities of our day-to-day work. We run courses in woodland gardening, sell plants on site and by mail order and organise regular volunteer working parties. Facilities are very basic at present. Visitors need to bring a tent or other living accommodation and need also to be able to provide for themselves. Currently we are three full-time members

Year started 1989
Ideological focus ecological

Blagdon Cross, Ashwater,
Beaworthy, Devon EX21 5DF England
Telephone 0845 4584719
Electronic Mail veganic@gardener.com
World Wide Web http://www.pfaf.org

with about ten possible future members. It
is early days yet. We ask visitors to chip in
on food to share for communal meals. We
also value our space and respect that in
others. We are a vegan project and ask
overnight visitors to respect this, to at least
be vegetarian on site and vegan in communal areas. Please contact us for further information.

POSTLIP HALL

●●●●●●●●●●●●●●●●●●●●●●●●●●●●●●●●●●●●●

Postlip Hall is tucked into a fold of the Cotswold Hills, surrounded by woods, with views out to Winchcombe, our local town. We are currently 8 families with ages ranging from mid sixties to in utero! Most people work outside as teachers, writers, artists, medics as well as environmental and social service employees. We operate as a Housing Association meeting every month, or more frequently, to help upkeep the Grade 1 listed building and 16 acres of ground. We work communally on the organic garden monthly and welcome visitors both to these weekends and "fun days" to help mantain and improve the estate.We keep sheep and chickens as well as numerous pets. Jobs are allocated according to skills or enthusiasm!

We hold events in the 13th century Tithe Barn, including the Cotswold Beer Festival,

Year started 1970

Postlip Hall, Winchcombe,
Cheltenham, Gloucestershire GL54 5AQ England
Telephone 01242 603797
Electronic Mail stuartandsally@medix-uk.com

barn dances and wedding celebrations to
help supplement the ground rent we all pay
monthly.
Children are an important part of living here
and they seem to revel in the space and the
opportunities that life here offers.
We have no philosophy as such, but try to
live lightly on the earth and leave Postlip a
better place for those who follow.

QUAKER COMMUNITY

The Community's aim is to enable people to grow together spiritually in a caring environment, living together with a sense of shared adventure. We look after ten acres of land; some of it is cultivated as organic vegetable gardens and forest garden. Most of the rest consists of woodland, ponds and a meadow and is managed as our nature reserve. The three families have self-contained accommodation, there are two flats and individuals have bedsits. There are communal rooms in the main house, including a kitchen/dining area where the whole Community can join together for Friday supper and Sunday lunch. We have wheelchair access to the ground floor. There is opportunity for corporate worship twice daily; on Sundays we host the local Quaker meeting. The Community has no hierarchy, and decision

Year started 1988
Ideological focus quaker

making at our weekly house meeting is
based on the Quaker business method.
Once a month we set aside time to share
feelings and reflect on our life together.
Members have a variety of occupations outside the Community. We keep chickens and
goats. Visitors are welcome at some of our
working weekends; please write with a
stamped addressed envelope.

RAINBOW HOUSING CO-OPERATIVE

ainbow (known by many as "The Street") is registered as an Industrial and Provident Society - a fully mutual housing co-operative. There are four three-storey, four-bedroomed houses and twenty, two-storey, two-bedroomed houses with a pedestrian way down the middle of the street. The aim of the group is to provide housing in a community setting and there is a communal garden with chickens and ducks (on a pond), organic vegetable growing facilities, play areas for the children and a large barbecue! The membership, usually between about 30 and 35, with about 20 children of all ages, is very mixed in age, sex and personal circumstances. One house (Nº9) is used as a Community House and has meeting space, office, laundry facilities, a workshop equipped with tools, deep freeze, domestic equipment and green-

Year started 1977

house. Provision has been made for disabled people with wheelchair access by means of a portable ramp and a toilet suitable for wheelchairs, accessible from indoors and outdoors. Many members are vegetarian or vegan,  although this is not a prerequisite for membership. Membership is by application and prospective members are expected to participate in the activities of the co-op, including work days and meetings, before being eligible for membership and therefore housing. It often takes some time before prospective members are successful, as the turnover of houses is infrequent and there are many people waiting.

REDFIELD COMMUNITY

How to describe Redfield? This community is one which, despite having been established more than twenty years ago, still has the feeling of vibrancy and experiment about it. The community is dynamic with the mix of members and their individual styles and personalities combining into the atmosphere we recognise as home. Our structure is that of a fully mutual co-operative and all our decision-making is by consensus at our weekly meeting. We live as a single household, cooking, eating, cleaning, gardening and working together. Practically speaking Redfield is a very busy place. Most of us have part-time jobs which we combine with working within the community. We manage the 17-acre estate ourselves and undertake some fairly substantial restoration and maintenance projects. We keep chickens and a flock of

Year started 1978
Ideological focus community life

lovely Jacobs sheep. We grow as much of
our own food as we possibly can, manage
the woodland and maintain the Victorian/
Georgian main house and all its outbuildings. We also host a number of visitors
throughout the year and run Living in
Commmunities weekend courses. No-one
ever complains of boredom at Redfield. We
all put a lot of energy in and we are repaid
in many ways. The satisfaction of complet-
ing a new roof on the stable block, the
mutual support we offer and accept from
each other, watching the children grow up
in this stimulating and nurturing atmosphere
and last
but not
least the
numer-
ous birth-
day
parties.

RUBHA PHOIL FOREST GARDEN

Our work takes place on a rugged and spectacular 15-acre wooded peninsula on the Sound of Sleite at the south end of the isle of Skye.

This area is known as the Garden of Skye because of the warming effect of the Gulf Stream. We share the promontory with the Armadale to Mallaig ferry and, because of this, we receive many local and global visitors. We also host school groups who come to visit our eco-info centre, herb gardens, worm and recycling areas and woodland walks to the seal islands. Our main income is derived from selling certified organic herb salads, plants and visitor donations. We live lightly and within our means.

Year started 1992
Ideological focus earth-ecological

Armadale Pier,
Isle of Skye, IV45 8RS Scotland
Telephone 01471 844700
Electronic Mail sandyrubha@aol.com
World Wide Web http://www.rubha-phoil.org.uk

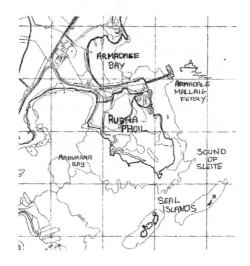

SALISBURY CENTRE

The Salisbury Centre, the longest-established holistic centre in Edinburgh, is a large Georgian house with lovely organic gardens; a peaceful haven in the city.

The Centre has offered courses focusing on spiritual, emotional and physical well-being for more than 28 years and can provide, at the Centre's direction, occasional overnight accommodation only for participants on many of our courses. The Centre has residential accommodation for up to six people and is open to applications as and when positions become available. The accommodation is tied with work in the Centre, running day-to-day business, gardening, maintenance and housekeeping.

Year started 1973
Ideological focus spiritual

Salisbury Centre
2 Salisbury Road,
Edinburgh, EH16 5AB Scotland
Telephone 0131 667 5438 **Fax** 0131 667 5438
Electronic Mail office@salcentre.ndo.co.uk

The heart of our work is to provide an
opportunity for growth for anyone seeking
to improve the quality of their life through
becoming more internally conscious and
aware.

SANFORD
HOUSING CO-OPERATIVE

We have beautiful ponds, gardens and a friendly atmosphere, a tropical communal oasis in London, with a famous colourful peace movement mural. Many performers and artists live here and we have tried to artistically redesign our living space. Founded in 1973 and built using private finance supplied by the Housing Corporation and Commercial Union, Sanford Housing Co-op consists of 133 units of shared accommodation in 14 purpose-built houses. Its rents are not set by any outside body but are designed to cover actual costs. All the tenants, as members of the Co-operative, are collectively landlords and responsible for helping the Co-op to protect their interests and to save the Co-op money by their voluntary work. Sanford actively seeks applicants from all sections of the community,

Year started 1973
Ideological focus co-operative/none

over the age of 18, who wish to live in a Co-operative, regardless of gender, ethnic origin, disability, sexual orientation or health status. Sanford is a single-person co-operative and is not suitable for applicants who have dependent children or who wish to live as a couple.

SCARGILL HOUSE

Scargill House is a holiday and conference centre in the Yorkshire Dales which opened in 1959 as a centre of evangelism and renewal for the churches in the North of England. Although it is an Anglican foundation, the original vision included staffing the centre with a Community of Christians from all walks of life and Christian denominations. Community members are divided into six teams — Chaplaincy, House, Kitchen, Pantry, Estate and Office covering the various functions of running what is basically a conference centre but with the addition of Christian input. All Community members have an opportunity of leading worship and of ministering to the guests. The prime purpose of the Community is to serve the guests. Community members eat in the dining room with the guests. The majority of

Year started 1959
Ideological focus christian

Scargill House
Kettlewell,
Skipton, North Yorkshire BD23 5HU England
Telephone 01756 760234 ext. 33 **Fax** 01756 760499

Community members are single, lay and young, but the Chaplaincy team comprises priests, women deacons and lay readers. The overall policy of Scargill House is the responsibility of the Council who are prominent members of the Church, both lay and ordained. The buildings accommodate 90 guests and, apart from several large lounges for conferences, there is a fine Chapel, Library, Quiet Room and Games Room. Enquiries for private bookings should be made to the Bookings Secretary, for conferences to the Conference Secretary and for Community membership to the Administrator.

SHEILING SCHOOL CAMPHILL COMMUNITY

• •

The Sheiling School Camphill Community is an independent residential school for children and adolescents aged 6-19 with special educational needs, situated on a beautiful estate of parkland and farmland on the edge of the small town of Thornbury, South Gloucestershire. Most co-workers involved in care, education and therapy are fully resident, living with the children in five households. Education is based on the Rudolf Steiner (Waldorf) Curriculum. The community is permeated by a non-denominational Christian ethos, particularly through the celebration of festivals.

Healthy nutrition is a high priority and all land activities follow the Bio-dynamic method. The farm and kitchen garden provide a plentiful supply of fresh milk, home-reared meat and organic vegetables. Care

Year started 1951
Ideological focus camphill/christian/organic

Thornbury Park, Park Road, Thornbury
Bristol, BS35 1HP England
Telephone 01454 412194 **Fax** 01454 411860
Electronic Mail mail@sheilingschool.org.uk
World Wide Web http://www.sheilingschool.org.uk

for the land is a basic concern of the community.

Young people interested in caring for children with special needs and an alternative way of life can join the community for one year or more as volunteer co-workers. Induction training forms part of the Foundation Year.

Salaries are not paid to anyone living in a Camphill community. The cost of food, lodging and all basic living expenses are covered by the community budget. In addition, £25 per week pocket money is paid to new volunteers.

SHRUB FAMILY

Our communal name and address is misleading. We are not a farm, don't live in a cottage and, if the 'family' brings images of Californian-style cults ... we're not a family! We are a practical, secular, dirty-handed, music-playing, screaming-kids community. Individual interests range from midwifery and politics to fine arts and drugs legislation. We don't have any particular communal ideal, although we follow a pragmatic quest for sustainability and the hope of, one day, developing low-cost, eco-friendly, self-build housing. We share a rambling 17th century farmhouse with room for a maximum of ten to twelve members. We are too small to accommodate communal businesses and most members earn their livings in conven-

Year started 1969
Ideological focus ecological

tional jobs. Although we are surrounded by beautiful countryside we are close to a busy road and motor-racing circuit. Combine this with the presence of two 18-year-oldish members and you will see that Shrub is clearly not a place for those seeking a life of quiet spiritual contemplation! Our mainly organic garden and polytunnel give us an increasing level of self-sufficiency in vegetables. Planting trees, large flower beds and herbs is a passion. We share communal costs and dedicate a day's work a week to the house and grounds. We welcome vistors, who should write giving a phone number. We are actively seeking new members both for the long and short term.

SIMON COMMUNITY
(LEEDS)

The Leeds Simon Community is a volunteer community working with homeless people in the city. We have around twenty members, but the core of the Community is four residential volunteers living in two houses in the Woodhouse area. The focus of the Community is work with rough sleepers, the hidden homeless and the transient. We concentrate on those unwilling or unable to accept existing provision. Much of our work is based on informal contact and is complementary to the work of other agencies.

As a Community, we are involved in daily outreach work, a weekly soup-run, a night-shelter project, a workshop group and resettlement support. We also campaign locally on homelessness issues.

We value communal living and voluntary

Year started 1999
Ideological focus social justice

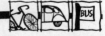

●●●●●●●●●●●●●●●●●●●●●●●●●●●●●●●●●●●●

action. We feel that social vulnerability
comes from a competitive society which
diminishes community life. Our ethos is
based on the belief that we have a personal
and communal responsibility for the socially
vulnerable in our society.

We try to reach decisions by consensus. We
eat communally several times a week, and
support each other in our work and life.
The Community is funded by public donations and we will shortly become a
Registered Charity. Full-time residential volunteers receive board, lodging and pocket
money. We are open to the idea of residential volunteers working part-time in paid
employment or living away from the
Community houses.

SIMON COMMUNITY (LONDON)

Simon is a community of rough sleepers and volunteers living and working together to care and campaign for street homeless people. We work for those who sleep rough as a way of life, those who are unable to accept existing help or for whom no adequate provision exists. We run a night shelter, residential houses of hospitality and a farm project. We also do extensive outreach work in order to make contact and build relationships with people living on the streets. We live and work in groups. Workers and residents share responsibility for decision-making and day-to-day running of the projects. We hold regular community meetings and daily breakfast meetings in each house. These meetings provide a forum for discussion and group support. The Simon Community needs both full and part-

Year started 1963
Ideological focus equality

Simon Community
PO Box 1187,
London, NW5 4HW England
Telephone 020 7485 6639 **Fax** 020 7482 6305
Electronic Mail simoncommunity@ic24.net

time volunteers. No previous experience is necessary, but humour, patience, tolerance and the ability to accept people for who they are will be essential qualities for adjusting to life in Simon. Workers must be at least nineteen years old and have a stable place to return to when they leave Simon. Room and board and pocket money are provided for full-time volunteers.

SOMEFRIENDS
COMMUNITY

F ervently eclectic (lively). Hard-edged niceness with cosmic bits. Maybe a little tough sometimes.
Challenging, random non-hierarchical. Regular meetings. Comfy consensus. Same monthly rent for all. There are mice, but there is a sliding scale for food. Three floors above a leather shop, East London. Large spacious, rambling. School and prostitutes at back. Many unwilling capitalists. Sesame and Rosie are cats but only one is active at present. And we have our own rooms.
Other useful information;
We have 3 eco balls.
300-500 worms some leaving soon with their German girlfriend.
Nice wine appreciated.
Visits can be arranged.

Year started 1973
Ideological focus various

Somefriends Community
c/o Diggers & Dreamers
Telephone 020 7739 6824
Electronic Mail Somefriendscommunity@hotmail.com

COMMUNITY OF ST FRANCIS

The Community of Saint Francis is an Active community in the Franciscan tradition in the Church of England. A commitment to regular corporate and personal prayer and study undergirds outreach of mission and caring work. At Compton Durville the sisters receive guests for rest, retreat and holidays: a large conference room is available for day groups or for projects. Other houses of the community are in urban priority areas where small groups of sisters are in part-time semi-vocational, sometimes salaried work. The community has no major funds and members have to assist in generating sufficient income. As a registered charity there is no fixed charge for guests but a donation is requested. The sisters share a common dining room with guests and chapel services are open to all. Some spirituality programmes are offered

Year started 1905
Ideological focus christian

Compton Durville,
South Petherton, Somerset TA13 5ES England
Telephone 01460 240473 **Fax** 01460 242360
Electronic Mail csf.compton@talk21.com
World Wide Web http://www.orders.anglican.org/ssf/

from time to time; also individually guided
retreats and Myers Briggs workshops.
Community members make traditional religious vows of poverty, celibate chastity, and
obedience, endeavouring to live these out
in an open spirit of life sharing and relationships. Decision-making is mutual, consulta-
tive and where possible, by consensus. An
elected chapter and officers operate as
appropriate.

STEPPING STONES HOUSING CO-OP

S tepping Stones is based on a 30-acre farm in the Wye valley, on the edge of the forest of Dean. We are committed to managing the land and renovating the 16th-century farmhouse. As a long-term aim we would like to turn this farm into a small prototype organic eco-village. We would like to hear from others who are particularly commited to working on or with the land in some way. We operate by consensus, and have regular meetings and subgroups to organise what we do here. We are opposed to all human, animal and ecological exploitation. We have a lot of children on site, some of us home educate and we are generally very child focused. We are members of Radical Routes, and are interested in helping others set up similar projects. We are working towards establishing small businesses and workers' co-ops on site. Visitors

Year started 1999
Ideological focus ecological

Stepping Stones Housing Co-op
Highbury Farm, Redbrook,
Monmouth, NP25 4LX Wales
Telephone 01600 713942
Electronic Mail highburyfarm@hotmail.com

are invited to make a contribution to living
expenses and participate in co-op work. If
you would like to visit please phone first to
make arrangements.

STEWARD COMMUNITY WOODLAND (AFFINITY)

We are seven woodland dwellers enjoying living and working in a 32-acre mixed woodland on the edge of Dartmoor. We are running a project to demonstrate the value of integrating conservation woodland management techniques (such as coppicing and natural regeneration) with organic growing, permaculture, traditional skills and crafts, and low-impact sustainable living.

We are living in bender-style dwellings, which include the communal Longhouse, the Kitchen, and a toolshed and workshop space. We have a micro hydro scheme and solar panels to generate electricity.

We spend our time gardening, coppicing, creating crafts, maintaining and improving our dwellings and infrastructure, on out-

Year started 2000
Ideological focus ecological

Steward Community Woodland, Moretonhampstead,
Newton Abbot, Devon TQ13 8SD
Telephone 01647 440233 **Fax** 07050 674 467
Electronic Mail affinity@stewardwood.org
World Wide Web http://www.stewardwood.org

reach work (such as green woodworking displays and cycle-powered workshops), and on working for social change. Our plans for the woodland include encouraging natural regeneration of native trees, providing demonstration permaculture and forest gardens, a woodland walk, a community composting scheme, and examples of renewable energy. We intend to run courses and have school visits to the gardens and nature trails. We welcome visitors for short or long stays (please phone first to arrange this). We also have a large, lively website that has our latest news and events alongside 'how to' guides, a photo gallery and much more.

STROUD COHOUSING COMMUNITY

Cohousing is defined quite formally by 5 criteria: parking on the periphery; regular meals in the communal house; buildings designed and built by members; non-hierarchical decision making; each household has a fully self-contained property. Cohousing is the most exciting way to live since people left caves.

The Cohousing Company Ltd was set up in May 2000 with 5 household members to develop the first new-build cohousing community in the UK. A 2-acre site in the centre of Stroud, Gloucestershire with out-line permission for 29 dwellings was bought in September 2000 for £550,000. A few months later 25 families/households had joined, each paying £5,000 for shares in the development company and pre-payments for their plot — the community was 80% pre-sold before detailed planning permission

Year started 2000
Ideological focus cohousing

4 Carlton Gardens,
Stroud, Gloucestershire GL5 2AH England
Telephone 01453 766466
Electronic Mail info@cohouses.net
World Wide Web http://www.cohouses.net

was received. The loan on the land was
soon re-paid in full. The Cohousing group
collectively agreed the layout and design of
each house, especially the large communal
house in the centre. Stroud Cohousing has
many ecological brownie points: rainwater
harvesting, super-insulation, solar panels,
car-sharing, daily communal meals etc.
Building is expected to start Nov 2001 and
to be completed in 2002.

The Cohousing Company
intends to build a sec-
ond Cohousing
Community in
2002/3, we
are looking
for land!

TALAMH

Talamh is Gaelic for earth / soil. The co-op currently houses 11 adults, 3 kids, 4 dogs, 3 cats, 2 horses, some goldfish, and a gerbil. It has a 17th-century farmhouse, cottage and outbuildings, with 50 acres of land. The land has, over the years, been transformed back from farmland to habitat, with over 5000 native broadleaf trees planted, and a large pond created to complement the wetland and grassland re-wilding itself. We also have organic vegetable gardens, a polytunnel, a young orchard, hayfield, and are bordered by streams on three sides, one of which we are working with to provide our energy needs with a micro hydro power system combined with solar panels and small-scale wind turbines. We aim to create alternatives through co-operative structures and to develop relationships of co-existence with creation. Locally we are surrounded by a motorway,

Year started 1993
Ideological focus environmental

Birkhill House,
Coalburn, Lanarkshire ML11 0NJ England
Telephone 01555 820555/820400 **Fax** 01555 820400
Electronic Mail talamh@lineone.net

and open-cast Mining, and see it as essential not just to oppose such things, but also to show viable physical and social examples of what can be made possible outside of profit-driven enterprise. We have formed an Environmental Education Charity, which at the time of writing is busy fundraising to develop an educational visitor centre and community resource. Part of the commitment as a member of Talamh Housing co-op, is a minimum of 14 hours per week voluntary work, on practical projects or administration. To join requires regular visits followed by a 2-month trial period and a commitment to our policies and those of Radical Routes (of which we are a member). All members have to agree to the new member joining. Food is Vegan/Vegetarian. Visitors are requested to take part in the household rota, and con-tribute work to the current projects, in return for food and board, we also request income-related donations towards costs.

TANGRAM
HOUSING CO-OP

Tangram is a registered Housing Co-operative. We have 40 units of accommodation, all in or near Bank Side Street in Harehills, Leeds. They range from studio flats through to four-bedroom family houses. We also have some communal accommodation. We are funded by the Housing Corporation (a government body), which means that we are regulated and can afford to keep our houses in a high state of repair.

The Co-op is run by the tenants with support from a part-time worker. All tenants are members of the co-operative and have to be voted in at a General Meeting.

As a tenant, you enjoy the following advantages: cheap rent (about £33 per week for a one-bed flat), a centrally heated flat or

Year started 1978
Ideological focus co-operative

house, a great repairs service, training and
advice if you need it, the control of being
your own landlord, and a friendly and welcoming community that cares for its members.

In return for this, we expect you to spend
about 2 hours a week helping to run the co-op.
As well as keeping rents down, this is a great
way of socialising with the other co-op
members.

TARALOKA BUDDHIST RETREAT CENTRE FOR WOMEN

Taraloka is both a community and a Buddhist retreat centre for women, to which women come from all over the world to experience the calm, beautiful atmosphere which has built up over the fifteen years of the centre's existence. All of us living here are comitted to Buddhist ideals and to creating the best possible facilities for women to come on retreat. For the purposes of our work, the community is divided into two teams, the Retreat Team and the Support Team, with one retired member. We all actively pursue the Buddhist way of life, following a daily programme of meditation, work and communal meals. There is a strong emphasis on ethical practice, aiming for more kindness, generosity, contentment, truthful speech and clarity of mind. Apart from our respective team meetings, we hold weekly community meetings and business

Year started 1983
Ideological focus buddhist

Cornhill Farm, Bettisfield,
Whitchurch, Shropshire SY13 2LD England
Telephone 01948 710646
Electronic Mail enquiries@taraloka.org.uk
World Wide Web http://www.taraloka.org.uk

meetings. We aim to be friendly and co-operative and decisions are arrived at through consensus. Taraloka is registered as a charity and all members receive the same basic support. We are all part of the Buddhist Movement of the FWBO (Friends of the Western Buddhist Order) and mainly offer retreats for people who have had some experience within that movement. We also run Newcomers Weekends where we introduce meditation and Buddhism and there is an Open Day each year.
For further information please contact our secretary.

TORCH
HOUSING CO-OP

W e're a Housing Co-operative that's been around for over 7 years, a mile or so away from the city centre in what is one of the most culturally diverse cities in Britain. We arose from the Radical Student population of the early 1990's via New Education Housing Co-op and are members of Radical Routes and take part in an awful lot of different things. We've got 2 big, beautiful houses 100 yds away from each other, one a 5 bedroom Georgian Style and the other an 8 bed-roomed Grade II listed mansion with office space and a big community room, both of which we rent out to other organisations or else use ourselves for parties, meetings etc. We are a lively group of people that like living collectively and are very diverse in both ages, views and diet, but are very definitely alternative. Our kitchens are collec-

Year started 1994
Ideological focus mixed

10 Richmond Road, Hockley,
Birmingham, West Midlands B18 5NH England
Telephone 0121 554 4256
Electronic Mail jantorch@netscapeonline.co.uk
or jantorch4@lineone.net

tively vegetarian and communal meals are
optional and arise spontaneously, along with
our parties. We are always looking for new
members to help us run everything and to
replace the ones that have moved on and if
you would like to find out more, drop us a
line. We are also open to visitors and friends
popping in, but ring us first.

TURNER'S FIELD

Turner's Field is a small, radical eco-settlement dedicated to education and demonstration of all aspects of sustainable living.

We have a special emphasis on sustainable social structure to empower individuals with consensus decision making, community building and personal empowerment, integrated into daily life.

Four acres, houses, veg, fruit, bees, sacred gardens, wildlife of all kinds, eco-philosophy, art, music, events.

We have a strong connection to the 'Avalonian' community in Glastonbury town and environment through LETS, Credit Union etc.

Year started
Ideological focus eco/taoism

Turner's Field
Compton-Dundon, Somerton,
Glastonbury, Somerset TA11 6PT
Telephone 01458 442192

THE WELL AT WILLEN

The Well is a large house in 3 acres of land located on the outskirts of Milton Keynes, next to Willen Lake. The community which was founded in 1997 has grown from a Christian base, however we welcome as members people of differing beliefs. Each family/individual has their own living space as well as sharing in the communal areas. We currently have seven adult residential members and five children. We are looking for new members.

As community members we aim to have a daily, shared meal and one act of reflection/prayer together, which is led by a different member of the community each week in accordance with their own beliefs. The daily tasks of the community (cooking, cleaning, shopping) are based on a rota

Year started 1997
Ideological focus ecumenical

The Well, Newport Road, Willen
Milton Keynes, MK15 9AA England
Telephone 01908 242190 **Fax** 01908 242187
Electronic Mail community@thewellatwillen.org.uk
World Wide Web http://www.thewellatwillen.org.uk

● ●

system. We are a housing co-operative. We
all pay rent on our private living quarters
and contribute towards food each week.
In choosing to live together we offer an
alternative to the prevailing trend of individ-
ualism. We offer hospitality and seek to promote Peace and Justice: this takes many
forms, including a project to support local
asylum seekers.

WOODHEAD COMMUNITY

Woodhead is continually evolving. It began with a vision and focus of being a land and family based spiritual community. Eight years on these original elements are more or less still in place, and we have broadened our perspective to include the needs and visions of the many people of different nationalities who have lived here. Our passions, skills and aspirations are as varied as the members. The spiritual dimension is central to us, but as an individual and personal practice, rather than as a collective one. Currently we are making space for personal creative expression. Maintaining and working with relationship is what gives juice to our community. Currently we consist of two families, one couple and two single adults. We have five children between us. We live in beautiful surroundings, valuing our garden, the

Year started 1994
Ideological focus collectively living with spirit

Woodhead, Kinloss,
Forres, Moray IV36 2UE Scotland
Telephone 01309 674000 **Fax** 01309 674000
Electronic Mail stephen@woodheadcom.org

local countryside, and our close proximity to
the Findhorn Foundation. We eat together
at least five nights a week, enjoying home-
grown food and companionship. We have a
weekly sharing/business meeting.
Discussions can be intense, fun and challenging at the same time. We are changing
to a more collectively owned structure,
though we have yet to decide on the format. When space is available we are open
to visitors and prospective new members.

WOOLMAN HOUSE

Woolman House is a small ecumenical Christian community in inner-city Liverpool. We seek to live in solidarity with oppressed people through offering hospitality to refugees, rejecting consumerism, and nonviolently resisting the causes of poverty in exploitation and militarism. We are inspired by the Catholic Worker movement and its founders Dorothy Day and Peter Maurin. Our name remembers John Woolman, the 18th-century Quaker slavery abolitionist and advocate of a simple lifestyle and radical nonviolence. Members support themselves through part-time paid work; this way we can offer our time and resources to refugees as a gift. We work in co-operation with local church communities and other volunteers, and help to run a weekly drop-in for refugees. Contemplative prayer is important to us,

Year started 1999
Ideological focus christian

c/o Diggers & Dreamers
Telephone 0151 2806967

and sometimes takes the form of political witness outside arms factories and government offices. Our other activities include singing, gardening and baking bread. We publish a newsletter, Sanctuary, three times a year.

AMADEA COHOUSING COMMUNITIES

c/o Penton Bungalow, 1 Penton Close, Pounds Hill
Crediton, Devon EX17 1DT
Telephone 01363 775502 **Fax** 0870 056 8418
Electronic Mail ron@blissout.demon.co.uk
WWW http://web.ukonline.co.uk/bristol.goodwill/amadea

Amadea's early focus was on a purpose built 'centre' for people in the last third of life, but other associated avenues were explored.

It is now a network of people and groups meeting locally to develop plans for community living with a spiritual focus. There is a centrally held depository of information and experience available to groups developing their own schemes and a regular Newsletter. We want to make our lives together creative, healing and fun.

We come from various walks of life but share a vision of community life which involves a deep concern for the planet and all who live on it. Many of us would like to employ permaculture principles, aiming at maximum sustainability and conservation of scarce resources. Some groups will build from scratch, others convert existing properties, with a range of possibilities for ownership or renting. Each group will develop its own guidelines and focus within the Amadea ideology, but is likely to have a shared sacred space, meeting room and shared use of utilities.

ANARRES

c/o Blackcurrent, 24 St.Michael's Ave, Northampton, NN1 4JQ
Telephone 01604 633203
Electronic Mail blackcurrent@lineone.net

We are intending to establish an ecovillage, in (or next to) a wood. We want to demonstrate that people can exist happily and healthily without degrading the environment, and that human communities are sustainable living elements of the natural world; to grow food and other useful plants veganically; a nonviolent philosophy; shared childcare; no motorised vehicles; preferably near to a Sustrans route; no livestock, pets or rescued animals; income pooling; doing without electricity, gas, fossil fuels or concrete. We don't want to move to the wood until we have a confident group of six to ten people who have lived together for at least a year at Blackcurrent (see separate entry). We are especially looking for people with skills and experience in: woodcraft (particularly with green wood); building with wattle and daub, wood and stone; well building without bricks; dentistry; forest gardening; no-dig veganic food production; coppicing; reed beds; clay woodstoves; making fabric and dyes from plants; clog making; plant and fungi identification. However, if none of this sounds like you, but you're enthusiastic, willing to learn and you share similar dreams to ours, please get in touch anyway.

Ideological focus nonviolence

CHANNEL ZERO HOUSING CO-OP

c/o 188 Woodhouse Lane, Leeds, West Yorkshire LS2 9DX
Fax 0113 2629365
Electronic Mail bluebell@archaeologist.com
WWW http://www.endymion.ukf.net/channelzero.htm

We are an embryonic housing co-op in Leeds, firmly committed to co-op values and trying to put them into practice and deeply committed to the vision of Radical Routes, to shared housing, and to eating together as one big happy (sometimes anyway ...) family. We will have a vegan kitchen. Due to our activist background we have developed a deep media scepticism and yearning for real DIY culture. We will have a robust no television on site rule/policy in order to be a refuge from televisual narcosis and have lots of fun. The BBC is the voice of Babylon. There is no such thing as good television, it is a form of social control at odds with any vision of peace and freedom.

We feel very strongly that in and through community lies the salvation of the world. Commitment to community building and maintenance (within the co-op and out in the world) has to be our first priority. There has to be more to a co-op than bricks and mortar. We feel that co-ops have to be built of caring for others, solidarity and love. Without love we would amount to nothing.

Ideological focus ecological

COHOUSING 2000

c/o Diggers & Dreamers
Electronic Mail lizmurray@ednet.co.uk

Cohousing 2000 is working to set up a cohousing scheme in the Edinburgh area. We intend to create a sustainable community, which combines the autonomy of private dwellings with the advantages of community living, is built using environmentally sensitive methods, and incorporates a pedestrian-friendly design. The community will have between twelve and thirty dwellings, depending on the size of the site, and a common house. It is our intention to create a mixture of house/flat sizes to suit different incomes, ages and needs within the community. We have been meeting since February 1997 and are looking for a suitable site. We are beginning to embark on the lengthy, but very exciting, design process and welcome new members.

We regularly hold introductory meetings, which look at cohousing in general and the aims and present situation of our own cohousing group. Please contact us for further details.

CREDITON COMMUNITY COHOUSING

c/o Penton Bungalow, 1 Penton Close, Pounds Hill
Crediton, Devon EX17 1DT
Telephone 01363 775502 **Fax** 0870 056 8418
Electronic Mail ron@blissout.demon.co.uk

Four of us (three adults and Esme - 3yrs) have been meeting since Septmber 2000, on a regular monthly basis, to build trust and good comunication skills. Using the community building techniques outlined in 'The Different Drum' by Scott M Peck we hope to set up a co-housing project in the South West.

We are attempting to find a heart-felt balance between the practical discussion/decision making process and quality time for silence and sharing. We are nourished by fun, creativity, earth centred spirituality and we practise ecological awareness wherever possible. We are learning as we go.

Individually, all three of us have had previous experience of community living - Beech Hill, Pilsdon Manor, Divine Light Ashrams and Gaunts House.

We are now actively looking for more like-minded people to join us so do contact us for more details. Overnight accommodation and camping (in the summer) can be arranged. Children are welcome.

Ideological focus right relationship

LANCASTER COHOUSING GROUP

Lancaster Cohousing group
c/o 38 Coverdale Rd,
Lancaster
Electronic Mail catandcoat@compuserve.com

Proposed Cohousing scheme to be located somewhere within a short walking distance of the centre of Lancaster. Very early days - 1st meeting Autumn 2001. It is envisaged that the community will be structured along co-operative lines with properties for both sale and to rent. A self-build option will also be considered for some of the properties. All the housing will be to a high enviromental standard and a common house with various shared facilities will be built including: communal kitchen/dining area, guest rooms, kids space(s), laundry (+other facilities yet to be decided.) An attempt will be made to address shared transport needs through looking at options for carpooling, electric/compressed-air vehicles, proximity of site to public transport/cycle tracks etc. It is hoped to attract a broad cross-section of people in terms of age, sex, sexual orientation, ethnic heritage and income capacity. Anybody interested in getting involved contact Chris Coates at the above address.

THE LAND OF ROOTS

The Land of Roots
14 Great North Road,
Newcastle Upon Tyne, Tyneside NE2 4PS
Telephone 0191 2602817

For several years this group has been growing, evolving, expanding, shrinking, searching, researching and changing. It is now a stable group of five members with an additional supporters' group and advisory group. We are currently hoping to buy 42 acres of woodland in County Durham this summer, 2001.

We now have half of the money and we need to raise a little more before we go to the bank for the rest.

Once bought we intend to establish an educational facility, start a timber and woodcrafts business, grow mushrooms, keep bees, build low-impact structures, grow willow, fruit and vegetables, make chairs and charcoal etc. The project is focused on a balance between business, community and personal development. We will be using permaculture design techniques.

The group currently consists of a permaculture designer, woodworker, willow sculptor, celebrant, researcher and many other skills beyond.

Ideological focus permaculture

THE LIVING VILLAGE TRUST

5-7 Castle Green, Bishops Castle, Shropshire SY9 5BY
Telephone 01588 638958 **Fax** 01588 638958
Electronic Mail living.village@btinternet.com
WWW http://www.livingvillage.com

❖●❖●❖●❖●❖●❖●❖●❖●❖●❖●❖●❖●❖●❖●❖●❖●❖

The Wintles site is going to be a new 'eco-neighbourhood' on a southwest slope adjacent to the South Shropshire town of Bishops Castle (population 1750). It is in some ways a conventional 'development' managed and funded by the Living Village Trust, but it has a strong self-build element. The houses face pedestrianised squares set with the community buildings around a central green. The upper part of the site (12 acres) is for horticulture and has been planted with woodland trees and orchards. On-site facilities will include workspaces, a Learning Studio (alternative school) and an Alms House. Heat, power, water and telecomms will be part of the site infrastructure. Residents will buy a 1000 year lease on a 'barn ready to convert' to enable self-build within our design code, or buy a finished house. Some houses may be for rent, but local people will have priority. Each household then has a share in the management company that owns the central green, amenity land and the services company. As of Spring 2001 about one third of the plots are spoken for, building infrastructure works start in September 2001.

Ideological focus realist (diggers)

OLDER WOMEN'S CO-HOUSING LONDON

Older Women's Co-housing London
PO Box 29777,
London, NW3 2RH England
Electronic Mail owch@lineone.net

This pioneering group, which began meeting in 1998, hopes to be resident by 2003-4 in a 24-unit environmentally friendly building within the Greater London area.

Restricted to women only aged 50 and over, there will be a balance of wholly-owned, part-owned and wholly rented individual, self-contained flats with communal facilities and activities.

Applicants for the community, which will be self-sustaining and self-managed, will be selected from a waiting list of those who regularly attend monthly meetings prior to residency. At these meetings, would-be members are responsible for forming policies, undertaking shared tasks and actively participate in communal activities, thus showing that they are committed to sharing the group's values. In this community all women will have an equal voice and will be welcomed equally irrespective of ethnicity, class, religion, political persuasion, sexual preference and physical ability. This non-hierarchical living group hopes to enhance the wellbeing of older women through co-operation, friendship and mutual support, while remaining active members of the wider community.

Ideological focus feminist

PROMETHEUS PROJECT COMMUNITY

c/o 31 Caerau Road, Caerau, Maesteg
Bridgend, Mid Glamorgan CF34 0PB Wales
Telephone 01656 739813 **Fax** 01656 739813
Electronic Mail robert-howes@totalise.co.uk

◆◇◆◇◆◇◆◇◆◇◆◇◆◇◆◇◆◇◆◇◆◇◆◇◆◇

The Prometheus Project is difficult to describe. In a word, ambitious. Community is important but so is much else, like inventions for better living, and the utilisation of ignored inventions and discoveries (like phages for disease control, or give and take stalls to show there's an alternative to money, and much else). Business is important too, we plan to run vegan hotels and a wide range of other businesses. Self-build eco-houses will be a focal point, and a tree nursery and veg garden. Business makes money, money buys land and other resources as well as creating jobs. Co-operatives are ideal but not the only way. No-one has a monopoly on what is right. Straight business, just for the money (and damn the consequences) is all wrong. Business to end business (ultimately) and make life our business, not money. That should be the goal. So if you want more than a community, share skills, spread ideas, lead the good life without tobacco and other deadly chemicals, think about joining us. Capital useful but not necessary. We have properties in South Wales and land in South Devon. We hope to move to South Devon soon to start eco-house building

Ideological focus ecobusiness

RED KITE COLLECTIVE

c/o Bronydd, Llangeitho,
Tregaron, Ceredigion SY25 6QG Wales
Telephone 01974 821519
Electronic Mail redkite@nobeard.freeserve.co.uk

We are a group of 6 adults & 9 children who intend to provide secure and reasonably priced housing in West Wales. We are looking for a 20-acre-plus property within the Ceredigion, preferably woodlands & areas for tree planting, permaculture & forest gardening. We hope to provide self-contained dwellings, a communal space, and to construct traditional, semi-permanent dwellings. We are dedicated to cooperative living, aiming to form our own social and community base as well as securing our individual housing needs. We want the opportunity to live a more sustainable and communal lifestyle, concentrating on custodianship of the land as a working alternative to the present status quo. We aim to produce food organically & deal with all our own waste products by the sharing of resources, skills and energy. The Co-op will actively promote low-impact structures, as well as investigating appropriate technology to live in an energy efficient, self sustaining, living environment. We hope to maintain individual autonomy, to allow the freedom to be creative, and to provide the social network to facilitate a policy of inclusion and tolerance. We intend to evolve wider links with the local community.

Ideological focus ecological

SHEKINASHRAM

c/o 4 Chalice Court, Silver Street,
Glastonbury, Somerset BA6 8BS
Telephone 0845 4582534
Electronic Mail info@shekinashram.org
World Wide Web http://www.shekinashram.org

The Shekinashram is being established as a spiritual community based upon the precepts of Peace, Unity and Truth. It is our intention to undertake an exploration of consciousness on all levels, ultimately establishing our Being in direct Divine Realisation.

We are committed to engaging a respectful relationship with all Life and intend to create a way of living that clearly demonstrates this. The community will be holistic, built upon eco-permaculture principles and will include low impact dwellings, organic food production and sustainable resource usage. We are committed to the continuing research and application of cutting edge green technology and to challenging old parameters, creating new paradigms of environmentally responsible and spiritually conscious lifestyle.

We aim to support the emergence, in the wider community, of a holistic worldview by offering a range of workshops from the contemplative through creative to the practical. We welcome new members who are enthusiastic and in alignment with our principles. Further details are available from us.

Ideological focus spiritual/ecological

SOUTH HAMS ECO-SPIRITUAL COMMUNITY

10a Riverside, Totnes, Devon TQ9 5JB
Telephone 01803 868744 **Fax** 01803 863022
Electronic Mail jkennaby@callnetuk.com

Our project involves self-building our Holistic Education Centre, with ecologically self-sustaining homes. Heightened by the recent foot-and-mouth epidemic, there is a great need in South Hams to re-employ farming people - with their local wisdom - into sustainable food and craft productive, smaller-scale localised businesses. These will have a holistic approach with permaculturally designed diversified mixed farms with craft permaculture woodlands. Our courses and experiential workshops are conceived to meet these realistic employment training needs, along with those seeking more creative, spiritually satisfying, diversified ways of life. To enable purchase of around 10 acres of mixed woodland and raise building costs we have formed a "benefit of the community not-for-profit society". Our members have a wide variety of skills and experience which they wish to offer to others via the courses, the building of the centre and eco-homes, and the establishment of permaculturally productive woodland gardens. We need new residents and members with skills and enterprise.

Ideological focus eco-spiritual

TRELOWAN SUSTAINABLE LIVING PROJECT

c/o Diggers & Dreamers
Telephone 01579 346487
Electronic Mail kvg@on-edie.net

T he Trelowan Sustainable Living Project was formed in
1999 with the aim of establishing an eco-hamlet committed to the principles of sustainable living. We are
currently based in South-East Cornwall and are seeking land in
a rural or a semi-rural locality. The Trelowan group currently
comprises 6 adults and 5 children, but would seek to expand
the membership in order to form a larger, more sustainable
community in time. The aim of the Trelowan project is to
create an ecologically-sustainable, land-based community
supporting people with diverse skills, interests and experiences,
who have a desire to live harmoniously together but where
there is a distinction between private and public space. We
aim to be an outward-looking community, working, trading
and sharing resources and skills with neighbours and the wider
community. The highest priority will be given to caring for the
environment through medium-impact development, nature
conservation programmes and minimising all sources of pollution. Through the development of a centre of excellence , a
showcase for options for sustainable living, we aim to improve
the overall quality of life in the local area by enhancing and
integrating aspects of the environment, housing, the economy,
health & education.

VEGAN COMMUNITY NETWORK

c/o Heart Sing, 2 Seaview Terrace, Tydraw, Bonymaen
Swansea SA1 7BD Wales
Telephone 01792 476737

The VCN is a loose coalition of vegans who share a common interest in intentional community, although some of us hold wildly differing dreams from each other. At the time of writing there is interest in a hotel in Swansea to be bought possibly by a small group of us. Malcolm Horne (01395 270280) remains interested in buying this hotel or another collective building to make accommodation and social space for vegans. Malcolm at present organises Devon Vegans and also runs the annual Vegan National Gathering. Bob Howes (01656 739813, robert-howes@totalise.co.uk) prefers to concentrate immanently upon businesses 'for vegans and potential vegans', principally recycling and vegan organic horticulture, but also property/accommodation. A piece of land in Devon and two houses in South Wales are already available. Bob is the last editor of the Vegan Community Project Newsletter. Welhealth is a vegan forest garden already up-and-running on two sites in North Wales. Contact Frank Bowman (07980 158661). There is a group possibly emerging who are interested in 'own front doors' in a village setting. We set up Vegan Hotels Ltd, a company that makes sharing (shares in) a property easier. One underlying aim is to develop a flexible open network, without the barriers presupposed by everyday commercial individuation.

Ideological focus vegan /near vegan

CREATING WELHEALTH CO-OPERATIVE

c/o Diggers & Dreamers
Telephone 01244 819088

●●●●●●●●●●●●●●●●●●●●●●●●●●●●●●●●●●

Creating Welhealth is an unincorporated co-operative, with trustees that hold land on behalf of the group. At present it holds 7 acres with a house and out-buildings in an idyllic setting just south of the Clwyd valley, North Wales, which is to be developed as a Fruit Farm.

Creating Welhealth's aims are to create sustainable vegan organic horticulture, and farms on which people can live their lives in harmony with the community and natural environment, as detailed in the Welhealth Constitution.

In practice this means Creating Welhealth is people who wish to build sustainable eco-areas, eco-farms or eco-villages that you can only live in if you live sustainably. Using sustainable technology such as renewable energy and materials. By caring and not harming or exploiting the local community; also the outer world community by living on your fair share of the world money cake and using the excess income to buy more land for others to join in. By being a loving, happy, sharing community at the land, and by caring and not harming the surrounding ecology, living in love and harmony with the surrounding ecology. Loving, not harming, using or killing animals.

Ideological focus sharing/co-operation

CAMPHILL COMMUNITIES UK

Gawain House, 56 Welham Road,
Norton, North Yorkshire YO17 9DP
Telephone 01653 694 197 Fax 01653 600 001
Electronic Mail info@Camphill.org.uk
World Wide Web http://www.camphill.org.uk

◊◊◊◊◊◊◊◊◊◊◊◊◊◊◊◊◊◊◊◊◊◊◊◊◊◊◊◊◊◊◊◊◊◊

Since its foundation in 1940, the Camphill Movement has made an essential contribution to the development of education, therapy and residential care for those with special needs. Camphill communities offer a diverse range of provisions in which vulnerable children, adolescents and adults, many with learning disabilities, live, learn and work with others in healthy social relationships based on mutual care and respect.

A Camphill Communities Guide provides information on each of the Camphill communities in the UK and the Republic of Ireland. Its principal aim is to inform and assist those responsible for the placement of children, adolescents and adults with special needs and those interested in working in Camphill as short-term or career volunteers. It also contains: an overview of the work of Camphill; information on training, development; and other initiatives associated with Camphill.

CATALYST COLLECTIVE

1 Gladstone Terrace, Lewes Road,
Brighton, West Sussex BN2 3LB
Telephone 01273 672186
Electronic Mail catalyst@co-op.org
http://www.subdimension.com/community/subversion/catalystcoll

◇◇◇◇◇◇◇◇◇◇◇◇◇◇◇◇◇◇◇◇◇◇◇◇◇◇◇◇◇◇◇◇◇◇◇◇

Catalyst Collective Ltd is a worker co-operative. We help people set up and register co-ops and in the last ten years over 100 housing co-ops, about 40 worker co-ops, a couple of charities, and a variety of different companies with co-operative aims have been registered through Catalyst. We have worked with various existing co-ops, as well as groups intending to set up co-ops; on issues such as group-working, legal structures, conflict resolution, financial viability of proposals, co-operation and meeting skills etc. Basically, we love working with and promoting co-ops (especially ethical & eco-friendly ones), and have a wide variety of skills & knowledge available.

We also actively encourage co-operation between groups of various types, and Catalyst is a member of (or actively involved with) Radical Routes, ICOM, ICOF, Confederation of Co-operative Housing, UK Co-operative Council, and The Co-op Party. If your group is considering setting up as a co-op, we can usually arrange for someone to come to speak to you. Please contact us if this would be useful. Obviously, where possible, we'd like to be paid for our work & time, but we enjoy our work so, as long as our travel costs are covered, we'll probably be happy to work with you (whether you can afford to pay us or not!).

CONFEDERATION OF CO-OPERATIVE HOUSING

Unit 19, 41 Old Birley Street, Hulme
Manchester, M15 5RF England
Telephone 0121 449 9588
Electronic Mail info@cch-uk.org

◊◊◊◊◊◊◊◊◊◊◊◊◊◊◊◊◊◊◊◊◊◊◊◊◊◊◊◊◊◊◊◊

The Confederation of Co-operative Housing is the national representative body for housing co-operatives. It is run democratically by its General Council, made up of housing co-op representatives from each English region and from supporter organisations. The CCH is mainly engaged in lobbying work, promotion, and research into housing co-ops and social exclusion. The CCH is working in partnership with the Co-operative Union, the Housing Corporation, the National Housing Federation, the Scottish Community Ownership Housing Forum, the Association for Tenant Involvement & Control and the All Party Parliamentary Group on Housing Co-operatives to create an environment where all people can make a realistic choice to live in a housing co-operative.

ECO-VILLAGE NETWORK FOR THE UK

Eco-Village Network for the UK
PO Box 1410, Bristol BS99 3JP England
Electronic Mail evnuk@gaia.org
WWW http://www.ecovillages.org/uk/network/index.html

◇◇◇◇◇◇◇◇◇◇◇◇◇◇◇◇◇◇◇◇◇◇◇◇◇◇◇◇◇◇◇◇◇◇

E VNUK is the UK branch of Global Eco-Village Network. We aim to encourage and help enable people and organisations in developing environmentally, socially and economically sustainable settlements. We promote sustainable settlement for all by acting as an information resource and news service and by maintaining a website listing eco-village projects, skills and resources. We provide current information on eco-village theories and practices, alternative technologies and sponsor workshops and events in order to increase public awareness of the issues.

THE FAMILY

Maxet House, Liverpool Rd
Luton, LU1 1RS
Electronic Mail info@thefamilyeurope.org
WWW http://www.thefamily.org/thefamily

◊◊◊◊◊◊◊◊◊◊◊◊◊◊◊◊◊◊◊◊◊◊◊◊◊◊◊◊◊◊◊◊◊◊

The Family is an international fellowship of independent Christian missionary communities. Our membership is comprised of over 90 nationalities and we are united in a firm belief that God's love is the solution to the problems that currently plague mankind. We live in over 1,425 Family communities in 101 countries on six continents.

The Family has three broad objectives: share with others the life-giving message of love, hope and salvation found in God's Word, the Holy Bible. We organize Bible classes and seminars, as well as teach the Bible on an individual level to interested people. Secondly, we try to be a living example of the love that we preach. Members perform regularly at musical benefits, serve as volunteers in disaster relief projects, and seek ways to provide comfort and material assistance to the disadvantaged. Our third objective is to ensure that each of our children receives a Godly upbringing in the best possible environment we can provide. Many of our members have chosen home-based education for their children. Most of The Family's fundamental beliefs and eschatological views are in line with those of millions of Christians the world over. We affirm the Bible to be the inspired Word of God; it is the basis and cornerstone of all our beliefs and practices.

NACCAN

Association of Christian Communities and Networks
Woodbrooke, 1046 Bristol Road, Selly Oak
Birmingham, West Midlands B29 6LJ England
Telephone 0121 472 8079

◊◊◊◊◊◊◊◊◊◊◊◊◊◊◊◊◊◊◊◊◊◊◊◊◊◊◊◊◊◊◊◊◊◊◊◊◊

The Association of Christian Communities and Networks is an ecumenical organisation whose membership includes individuals, long-established religious orders, new communities, groups formed around contemporary issues as well as groups from diocesan/ district and parish/local settings. Members share a belief in the power of small groups to make our world a more human place and seek the renewal of society and the church in a host of different ways. Members give their energy and enthusiasm so that they form a network where help, support, advice, information and encouragement are available. They receive a regular magazine containing articles, comments and news and participate in an annual general assembly. We are a movement whose members seek to be a voice within the churches to ensure that the living reality of community and the transforming power of small Christian groups is recognised.

RADICAL ROUTES

16 Sholebroke Avenue, Chapeltown,Leeds, LS7 3HB
Telephone 0113 262 9365
Electronic Mail cornerstone@gn.apc.org
WWW http:/www.radicalroutes.org.uk

◇◇◇◇◇◇◇◇◇◇◇◇◇◇◇◇◇◇◇◇◇◇◇◇◇◇◇◇◇◇◇◇◇·

Radical Routes is a network of radical co-ops working for social change. It is an independent secondary co-op formed by independent primary co-operatives. The day-to-day operation of Radical Routes is funded by service payments from its member co-operatives, by interest on loans and by donations. Money invested in Radical Routes is used to provide loans to its members. The members are currently registered housing and worker co-operatives actively working towards social change, but we are in the process of expanding to include other groups (eg radical social centres). Each co-operative participates in the running of the organisation, each has one vote and is fully involved in decision making. Finance is raised through the sale to individuals and businesses of shares in Rootstock, the ethical investors' co-op which only invests in Radical Routes.

Radical Routes publishes "How to Set Up a Housing Co-op" and "How to Set Up a Workers Co-op" for £5 each, and a Directory of Member Co-ops and Introduction to Radical Routes for £1.50 each. Well-hidden cash or cheques/PO made payable to Radical Routes should be sent to the enquiries address. Enquiries about ethical investment in Rootstock to: 50 Whateley Road, Handsworth, Birmingham B21 9JD, **Telephone** 0870 458 1132, http://www.rootstock.co.uk

Hockerton Match-Making Service

Are you looking to join a sustainable community but can't find one?
Are you struggling to find others to start a new sustainable community?
Are you a developer looking for buyers for your eco-homes?
If yes, this service is aimed towards you...
We are developing a service to put people in contact with each other,
thereby helping projects and people to develop their plans much
faster.

The service will provide:

- Regular contact lists of people and projects
- Early notification of new projects
- Assistance in finding contacts to develop your plans, including;
  green architects, manufacturers/suppliers of green materials and
  organisations/businesses providing specialist advice

If you are interested please send us an email requesting an initial
registration form: hhp@hockerton.demon.co.uk, or a 1st class A4 SAE.
(see Hockerton entry, p104)

visit our website!

www.diggersanddreamers.org.uk

For more books about communal living
and holistic cultural change have a look
at the Edge of Time website:

www.edgeoftime.co.uk

Boxed sets of Diggers & Dreamers,
1990-2001 still available! →

A=anthroposophy **B**=buddhist **C**=christian **Q**=quaker **S**=spiritual but non-specific **vtn**=vegetarian **vgn**=vegan
open in principle the community is open, in principle, to new members, although it may be full at present

	location	number of adults	number of children	open in principle	charge visitors?	volunteers?	regular communal meals?	dietary regime	spiritual focus	page
The Abbey	rural	5	●	●	●		●	vtn	C	28
Ashram	urban	60	8	●	●		●	vtn	C	30
Balnakeil	rural	35	11						N	32
Beech Hill	rural	11	5	●	●		●		N	34
Birchwood	rural	11	4	●	●	●	●		N	36
Blackcurrent	urban	5	2	●				vgn	N	38
Bognor L'Arche	urban	40							C	40
Bradwell Othona	rural	3	2		●	●	●		C	42
Brambles	urban	8	0					vgn	N	44
Braziers	rural	12	2	●	●	●			N	46
Brithdir	rural	13	8	●	●	●	●	vtn	N	48
Brotherhood	rural					●	●	vtn	C	50
Camphill Murtle	urban					●	●		A	52
Canon Frome	rural	30	19			●	●		N	54
CAT	rural	11	1			●	●		N	56
Clanabogan	rural	80	13	●					A	58
Clays Lane	urban	470	●						N	60

220

Community								Region	Page
Community Project	rural	36	25	●		●		N	62
Corani	urban	4	2	●		●		N	64
Cornerstone	urban	14		●		●	vtn	N	66
Coventry Peace	urban	3	1	●	●	●	vtn	N	68
Crabapple	rural	6	2	●	●	●		N	70
Cwrt y Cylchau	rural	4		●	●	●		N	72
Darvell Bruderhof	rural	160	150	●	●			C	74
Equinox	urban	6		●		●	vgn	N	76
Erraid	rural	10	1	●	●	●		S	78
Findhorn	rural	138	17	●	●	●		S	80
Fireside	urban	7	6	●		●		N	82
Fox	rural	10	1	●	●	●	vgn	N	84
Frankleigh	rural	15	17	●	●	●		N	86
Gaunts	rural	40	0	●	●	●	vtn	S	88
Glaneirw	rural	10	9	●	●	●		N	90
Glyn Abbey	rural	18	8	●	●	●		N	92
Grail	urban	14		●		●		C	94
Grimstone	rural	10	1	●	●	●		N	96
Gwerin	urban	21	1	●	●	●		N	98
Heartwood	rural	4	1	●	●	●	vtn	S	100
Hive	inner-city	5						N	102
Hockerton	rural	8	11	●	●	●		N	104
Holy Rood	urban	24						C	106
Keveral	rural	14	2	●	●	●		N	108

location	number of adults	number of children	open in principle	charge in principle	large visitors?	volunteers?	regular communal meals?	dietary regime	spiritual focus	page
Laurieston	rural	23	5	●					N	110
Aston Lee Abbey	urban	6		●			●		C	112
Little Grove	rural	7		●					N	114
Losang Dragpa	rural	25	1	●	●		●	vtn	B	116
Lothlorien	rural	12		●	●		●	vtn	B	118
Madhyamaka	rural	33		●	●		●	vtn	B	120
Monimail	rural	4		●			●		N	122
Monkton Wyld	rural	14	5	●	●		●	vtn	N	124
Mornington Grove	urban	11	3	●		●		vtn	N	126
Neighbours	urban	9	7	●	●		●	vtn	C	128
New Education	semi-rural	3	1	●	●			vgn	N	130
Old Hall	rural	38	15	●	●	●	●		N	132
Parkdale	urban	3		●			●	vtn	S	134
Parsonage	rural	6	3	●					N	136
Pennine	rural	40	30	●	●	●	●		A	138
P I C	rural	10	6	●		●			N	140
Pilsdon	rural	40	5	●	●				C	142
P F A F	rural	3	1	●		●		vgn	N	144

Community	Type									Page
Postlip	rural	15	11	●	●	●	●		N	146
Bamford Quaker	rural	13	8	●	●	●	●	vtn	Q	148
Rainbow	urban	34	20		●	●	●		N	150
Redfield	rural	15	7	●		●	●		N	152
Rubha Phoil	rural	4		●		●	●		N	154
Salisbury	urban	4				●	●	vtn	S	156
Sanford	urban	130				●			N	158
Scargill	rural	35	5	●		●	●		C	160
Sheiling Thornbury	rural	40	25			●	●		A	162
Shrub Family	rural	6	3	●			●		N	164
Simon, Leeds	urban	3	0			●	●		N	166
Simon, London	urban	60	0	●			●		C	168
Somefriends	urban	17				●	●	vtn	N	170
St Francis	mixed	7		●		●	●		C	172
Stepping Stones	rural	12	5	●		●	●	vtn	N	174
Steward	rural	8			●	●	●	vgn	N	176
Stroud Cohousing	urban	50	40			●	●	vtn	N	178
Talamh	rural	11	5	●		●	●	vtn	N	180
Tangram	urban	45	20				●		N	182
Taraloka	rural	12	0	●		●	●	vtn	B	184
Torch	urban	4			●		●		N	186
Turner's Field	rural	3	2		●		●		S	188
The Well	urban	7	5				●		C	190
Woodhead	rural	8	5	●	●	●	●	vtn	S	192
Woolman	urban	3		●		●	●		C	194

USEFUL CONTACTS

LEGAL STRUCTURE EXPERTS

Industrial Common Ownership Movement (ICOM)
74 Kirkgate, Leeds LS2 7DJ
Tel: 0113 246 1738

Co-operative Development Agency (CDA)
To find your local CDA, contact ICOM. The CDA can set you up with model rules/ Memorandum & Articles.

MONEY

Triodos Bank
Brunel House, 11 The Promenade, Clifton, Bristol, BS8 3NN
Tel: 0117 973 9339

Ecology Building Society
18 Station Road, Cross Hills, Nr Keighley, West Yorkshire BD20 7EN
Tel: 01535 635933
info@ecology.co.uk

Radical Routes and **Rootstock**
See p 218

OTHER USEFUL ADDRESSES

The International Communal Studies Association (ICSA)
Yad Tabenkin, Ramat Efal 52960, Israel
Fax: +972 3 5346376
yadtab@actcom.co.il

In The Sticks,
Market House, Market Place, Alston, Cumbria CA9 3HS
Tel: 01434 38680
http://www.inthesticks.com
A weekly newspaper full of advertisements for wierd and wonderful properties.

The Free Land and Property Book
by John Fortune
Success Books, Maple Marketing (UK) Ltd, 11 Knowsley Avenue, Southall, Middlesex UB1 3AX
Tel: 020 8813 9868
... you can claim valuable land and property in your area and make it yours. You might not believe that this is possible. In fact it is ... Phone for current price.

WWOOF

19 Bradford Road, Lewes, East Sussex BN7 1RB

We hope that you have found this edition of D&D to be both useful and enjoyable. We welcome feedback and invite you to fill out this postcard and return it to us.

What features did you like best about D&D 2002/2003?

What features would you add to a future edition?

What features would you leave out of a future edition?

How did you hear about Diggers & Dreamers?

Name
Address

Postcode
☐ We will continue to mail you about this and other publications distributed by Edge of Time unless you tick this box

If you bought this book from a retailer other than Edge of Time then send in this card to claim a copy of the 24 page booklet
How to do it ... while stocks last!

Diggers & Dreamers
PUBLICATIONS

Diggers & Dreamers
BCM Edge
London
WC1N 3XX